THE COMMONWEALTH AND INTERNATIONAL LIBRARY
Joint Chairmen of the Honorary Editorial Advisory Board
SIR ROBERT ROBINSON, O.M., F.R.S., LONDON
DEAN ATHELSTAN SPILHAUS, MINNESOTA
Publisher: ROBERT MAXWELL, M.C., M.P.

LIBRARIES AND TECHNICAL INFORMATION DIVISION
General Editor: G. CHANDLER

HOW TO FIND OUT IN
ELECTRICAL ENGINEERING

HOW TO FIND OUT IN
ELECTRICAL ENGINEERING

A guide to sources of information arranged according to the Universal Decimal Classification

BY

JACK BURKETT, F.L.A.

AND

PHILIP PLUMB, F.L.A.

PERGAMON PRESS

OXFORD · LONDON · EDINBURGH · NEW YORK
TORONTO · SYDNEY · PARIS · BRAUNSCHWEIG

Pergamon Press Ltd., Headington Hill Hall, Oxford
4 & 5 Fitzroy Square, London W.1

Pergamon Press (Scotland) Ltd., 2 & 3 Teviot Place, Edinburgh 1

Pergamon Press Inc., 44–01 21st Street, Long Island City, New York 11101

Pergamon of Canada Ltd., 6 Adelaide Street East, Toronto, Ontario

Pergamon Press (Aust.) Pty. Ltd., 20–22 Margaret Street,
Sydney, New South Wales

Pergamon Press S.A.R.L., 24 rue des Écoles, Paris 5e

Vieweg & Sohn Gmbh, Burgplatz 1, Braunschweig

Printed in Great Britain by Sydenham & Company Ltd., Oxford Road, Bournemouth

(3023/67)

Contents

List of Figures

Preface

THE purpose of this book is to provide for the first time a systematic and reasonably comprehensive guide to the many documentary sources of information covering electrical engineering and its various branches. Its design has been influenced by the experience gained in catering for the reading and information requirements of different levels of user in engineering research organizations, manufacturing firms and academic establishments.

The value of such a systematic approach to information sources cannot be exaggerated, particularly in this virile industry where ignorance of progress elsewhere means wasteful duplication of research effort and the production of uneconomically viable goods. This guide, therefore, is eminently suitable for all those librarians and information officers who are in any way concerned with electrical engineering either as a primary subject or as a peripheral interest. It will also be of value to practitioners at all levels, working on their own, thereby enabling them to exploit fully the wealth of literature that exists. Chapter 2— The Organization of Information—accommodates this kind of reader by including discussion on libraries and how to use them.

This book is also aimed at another very large group of readers —students and their teachers at various levels: from the higher grades of secondary school, through college and university, and up to postgraduate research. Formal training in the use of literature, an obvious student requirement, is rarely included in the academic syllabus. This work, therefore, fills the gap and caters for this need by leading the student successively through different stages and encouraging the careful examination of source material by including questions at the end of certain chapters. A

more specific kind of user intended is the student undertaking
bibliographical training at library schools in Great Britain and
overseas.

The choice of the Universal Decimal Classification as the
basis of arrangement of chapters was influenced by the wide use
that is made of this scheme by a great number of technical
libraries in different countries. Because of its similarity with the
Dewey Decimal Classification, however, no problem is created
for users of other libraries.

CHAPTER I

Careers for Electrical Engineers

Scope

RAPID growth in material prosperity experienced by highly industrialized countries is closely tied to the development of electrical engineering. It is a technology so pervasive that very few industrial, domestic, and social activities can be sustained without its continuing advances. The introduction of electric power sources in fact is the first essential to any developing country seeking to advance its standard of living.

Electrical engineering as a technology is no longer concerned only with the generation, transmission, and distribution of electric power, even though it remains the most important core activity. Ever-increasing demands for power are the constant stimulus for improved or new methods of production, and vast sums of money are spent on research and development leading to greater generating capacity. The scope of the industry is now so wide that it involves many other sciences and technologies, particularly physics, mathematics, chemistry, metallurgy, statistics, medicine, mechanical, and production engineering.

One of the most rapidly developing sections of the industry is electronics, a technology that has extended its influence into so many different spheres and is employing in Great Britain more than 300,000 people. Its products are used in the home, for entertainment, in industry, for defence, in communications and navigation, in medicine, for nucleonic instrumentation, and research apparatus. Closely associated with electronics is data processing, a young and very vigorous industry that is having revolutionary influence on research and production methods.

Telecommunication engineering is another area involving extensive research and development effort with far-reaching results.

For young people seeking a career, the electrical engineering industry offers a very wide choice of activity. Subjectwise it ranges from nuclear power stations to the design and manufacture of fractional horsepower motors, taking in power generation (complete stations—coal, gas, or oil-fired, nuclear and hydro) and components—generators, transformers, rectifiers, switchgear, and fusegear; power distribution; industrial and domestic utilization; lighting and heating equipment; traction and propulsion; measuring and control instruments, etc.

There is also a wide variety of applications to choose from according to qualification and personal inclination. Research may be either fundamental, concerned, for example, with the properties of materials or applied to adapting known principles to new processes. Design and development work attracts many professional engineers because it serves as a compromise between the academic discipline of research and practical and immediate demands. This type of work involves "the use of scientific principles, technical information, and imagination in the definition of a mechanical structure, machine, or system to perform pre-specified functions with the maximum economy and efficiency" (Report of the Fielden Committee on Engineering Design, HMSO, 1963).

An enormous range of jobs exist in the various manufacturing stages: preproduction planning, production control, operation and maintenance—each of which is concerned with the application of electrical engineering principles but also requires the facility of understanding people and the knowledge of the theory and practice of various kinds of equipment. There is also scope for travelling in this country and abroad where plant erection and installation are concerned. Apart from the technological side of electrical engineering, opportunities also exist in commercial applications for sales and contracts engineers. The requirements here are for technical ability combined with business acumen.

The type of employment available naturally varies according

to ability and qualification. In the manual grades are the electricians—mostly concerned with installation work, and the fitters—working to assembly drawings and accurate dimensions. Then there are the craftsmen, using their skills for processing and forming materials, and the technicians, "responsible for the bulk of the work in successfully implementing design. The number of competent technicians required is very large. Many technicians carry considerable responsibility, are little short of the professional engineer in ability, and have a high degree of control in industry" (Report of the Fielden Committee on Engineering Design, HMSO, 1963). Recruits with academic or professional qualifications enter the engineer, scientific officer, or experimental officer grades.

The choice of place of employment is also wide. A considerable amount of research and development in the fields of electrical and electronic engineering is undertaken in various government establishments. These include the Post Office, the Radio Research Station, the Royal Radar Establishment, Government Communications Headquarters, the Services Electronics Research Laboratory, the research stations of the Ministry of Aviation—the largest of which is the Royal Aircraft Establishment, and the Army, Navy, and Air Departments of the Ministry of Defence.

A very large employer of engineers, scientists, technicians, and craftsmen is the Central Electricity Generating Board, the authority responsible for the generation and bulk supply of electricity in England and Wales. Research and development on a wide variety of problems is undertaken in the three large headquarters' laboratories at Leatherhead, Berkeley (near Bristol), and Marchwood (in Hampshire), five regional research organizations, and some of the power stations. There are also four project groups responsible for the construction of new generating stations and extensions to the national grid. This is a large and expanding industry with a future; during the past 8 years output has doubled. A similar statutory authority with certain common interests is the United Kingdom Atomic Energy

Authority which offers at Harwell, Aldermaston, Risley, and elsewhere a wide choice of work in fundamental and applied research and in the development of new methods and systems. There is a regular requirement in particular for electronics engineers to investigate such problems as fast-counting circuitry, telemetry, automic control, and the design of analogue and digital computers. Then there are the government-sponsored industrial co-operative research associations most of whom are involved in one or more aspects of electrical and electronic engineering. The most relevant one is the Electrical Research Association, covering a wide range of problems affecting the electrical industry as a whole.

The variety of opportunities in industry is even wider and ranges over every aspect of the subject field. Electrical engineering firms range from the few giant companies such as the Associated Electrical Industries, English Electric, and the General Electric Company, each employing well over 60,000 people and manufacturing a wide range of electrical products, to very small firms with a few employees doing contract work and providing local installation and maintenance services.

All the large- and medium-sized firms make a substantial investment in research and devclopment. Associated Electrical Industries Ltd., for example, with over 90,000 employees spends several million pounds each year on research. The English Electric Company Ltd., employing over 80,000 people and maintaining more than ten separate works or divisions, has two central research establishments in addition to the activities of its allied and associated companies. Of the 65,000 employed by the General Electric Company 2500 are graduates or have equivalent qualifications. Electric and Musical Industries Ltd. employs 12,000 people, 9000 of whom are engaged in electronics; of these 40 per cent are working on research and development. An example of a smaller firm with specialist applications is Ultra Electronics, where 450 of its 1500 employees are engaged in aspects of research and development. There are many other firms like it. IBM, for example, at Winchester, the largest IBM laboratory outside the USA, employs over 600 people, about two-thirds of whom are professionally or technically qualified persons.

For the young person leaving school, college, or university, adequate facilities are offered by all of these organizations for training. The electrical engineering industry as a whole is progressive in its training methods and adaptable to suit individual requirements and aptitudes. Graduate direct entrants, for example, may receive basic and functional training for any period up to 2 years to link the gap between academic knowledge and current engineering technology and practice.

Student apprenticeships are available for GCE A-level recruits lasting 4–5 years. They take the form of sandwich courses involving alternating periods of practical work and full-time study and they normally lead to a degree or Higher National Diploma in Electrical Engineering. GCE O-level students may be granted 2-year full-time or sandwich courses leading to the Ordinary National Diploma. Alternatively, the O-level entrant can study by part-time day release for a Higher National Certificate. If he has broadly completed the examination requirements of Parts 1 and 2 of the Institution of Electrical Engineers by the time he has completed his apprenticeship (normally 5 years), he may be granted day release to study for Part 3. A very able student could be granted a sandwich course part way through his apprenticeship to enable him to obtain a degree or the Higher National Diploma.

Time off for part-time study is granted to technician apprentices involving 2 years for the Ordinary National Certificate and a further 2 years for the Higher National Certificate. A qualified technician might then be accepted for HND or degree courses.

Other facilities may include university scholarships awarded to outstanding boys who intend to read for an honours degree in mechanical, electrical or electronic engineering; financial assistance for postgraduate studies in the United Kingdom or abroad; and vacation training for undergraduates.

Professional Qualifications

The major professional institution in the United Kingdom for the electrical engineering field is the Institution of Electrical Engineers, corporate membership of which confers the title of "chartered electrical engineer". To attain this membership, applicants must have passed the Institution's examinations or claim exemption through possessing a degree or diploma of technology (now recognized as a degree). Associate members must also have at least 2 years' approved practical training and a further 2 years in a responsible position. Members must have been associate members for at least 3 years and have been doing work in a responsible post for at least 5 years.

The Institution covers the whole field of electrical engineering and it has four specialized sections covering measurement and control, electronics and communications, electricity supply, and utilization. Associate membership of the IEE is the accepted qualification of technical competence. The training programmes available in government, research, and industrial establishments, therefore, are designed towards this end. The IEE, in association with the Department of Education and Science, is responsible for awarding national diplomas and certificates in electrical engineering.

The equivalent organization for radio and electronic engineers is the Institution of Electronic and Radio Engineers. Specialist groups cover medical electronics, computers, radar and navigational aids, and audio-frequency engineering. Members must be at least 30 years of age and have passed the Institution's examination (or claim exemption). In addition, they must have been working for at least 10 years as radio or electronic engineers and have spent not less than 5 years in a responsible position. Associate members have a minimum age limit of 27 and a period of 5 years as radio engineers, 3 of which should be in a position of responsibility. Both of the British institutions have published recently careers pamphlets which discuss academic qualifications and list institutions offering different courses. Information concerning exempting qualifications and the Institution's own examinations is also available.

The equivalent body in the USA, the Institute of Electrical and Electronics Engineers, is not an examining body. Membership in various grades is conferred on individuals who have attained a demonstrated level of technical achievement. Membership of the IEEE therefore does not confer on any member any legal status as a professional engineer.

Other countries have similar societies but some have no recognized national engineering society. In such cases technolgists may form groups affiliated to the appropriate British institution.

References

Two good guides to the range of careers and training facilities are:

WHEATLEY, D. E. (Editor) *Industry and Careers: a study of British industries and the opportunities they offer.* London, Iliffe, 1961. 776 pages.

Yearbook of Technical Education and Careers in Industry. London, Black.

Other useful publications:

BRANDENBURGER, B. *Working in Television.* London, Bodley Head, 1965.

GERARD, G. *The Young Man's Guide to Electrical Engineering.* London, Hamish Hamilton, 1961. The emphasis is on generation and transmission.

LONGMATE, N. *Electricity as a Career.* London, Batsford, 1964.

SMITH, R. J. *Engineering as a Career*, 2nd edn. McGraw-Hill, 1962.

TREWMAN, H. F. *Engineering as a Career*, Batsford, 1964.

TREWMAN, H. F. *Electronics as a Career*, Batsford, 1962.

Available from Her Majesty's Stationery Office are the careers pamphlets of the Central Youth Employment Executive, including *Professional Engineers* and *Radio and Television Services* and another from the Civil Service Commission, *Engineers in the Government Service*, 1964.

In addition, informative booklets for different types of entrant are freely available from the Central Electricity Generating Board, the Electricity Council, the British Broadcasting Corporation, the United Kingdom Atomic Energy Authority, and from many industrial organizations.

Recommended publications for American opportunities are:

FEDER. *Electronic Engineering.* New York, Popular Library. Library.

UNIVERSITY OF MISSOURI. *Electrical Engineering.* Rolla.

ELECTRONIC INDUSTRIES ASSOCIATION. *Electronics: your chance to shape the future.* Washington.

The Organization of Information

Problems of Control

TECHNOLOGICAL progress is impossible without research and development, but progress can be painfully slow and uneconomical without the knowledge of what has been done in the past and what is currently being done elsewhere. This knowledge, of course, may not necessarily come from the literature, particularly when answers are required to immediate problems. A survey of the electrical and electronics industry made in 1956 by Christopher Scott and Leslie T. Watkins (Central Office of Information, Social Survey, London) reveals that technologists rely for this type of information mostly on either personal advice from colleagues, their own background experience, or practical solutions worked out in the laboratory. Literature is required, nevertheless, for checking physical constants and established theories, or for descriptions of processes and equipment. Literature plays an important part, however, in providing ideas or stimulation for improvements or new methods.

With the advance of technological progress, the volume of published information covering electrical and electronic engineering and associated topics grows rapidly. There are numerous national and international conferences, each yielding hundreds of papers, many of which are worthwhile; thousands of articles appear in technical journals; many new patents of invention are published in different countries; and a great number of technical specifications and pamphlets are regularly issued by the electrical companies of the world. In addition, there is the constant flow of books for different readership requirements. Consequently, it has become practically impossible for the scientist and the technologist to be sure that nothing of significance has been missed, even assuming that a substantial amount of time is devoted regularly to reading.

The correct and expeditious processing of scientific and technical information is a vital factor if we seriously intend to keep pace with the growing demands being made on technology. Without effective bibliographical control there is every chance that research may be duplicated unintentionally (see J. Martyn, Unintentional duplication of research, *New Scientist* **21,** 338 (1964)) or outmoded processes and equipment used longer than necessary.

The problem is aggravated by the great variety of publishing organizations in existence. Information of value is regularly distributed by international bodies, government departments and research centres, nationalized industries, research and development associations, learned and professional societies, academic establishments, industrial firms and, very extensively, by the commercial publishing houses. Another difficulty impeding effective control is the number of different forms of publication, for example: books, periodicals, reports, conference papers, trade literature, microtext, standards, patents, statistics, theses, and films. There is, of course, the increasing difficulty of coping with foreign languages and the need for efficient translation services.

Properly organized this great variety of technological information can be exploited effectively, but most economically through trained information librarians or workers. It is unfortunately a fact that in every industrial country there will always remain a large number of small units unable to provide their own full-time information specialists. There are a number of ways, nevertheless, in which such organizations can be assisted, and these will be discussed later. With or without well-staffed libraries of their own, many users of literature like to have some knowledge of sources. It gives them the ability to work independently, at least on relatively uncomplicated questions, and this is all to the good, for it releases the librarian for the more complex and difficult searches. Then there are the library specialists in other subject areas who need bibliographical guidance in an unfamiliar field.

Bibliographies

The need for published guides to information sources cannot be overstressed, for bibliographical control is a sizeable problem. Apart from the volume of literature and multiplicity of forms which we have already mentioned, selection of material is rendered difficult by the varying levels of approach and the duplication of effort that exists between different publishers. There is also the problem of datedness in technological publications in relation to usage value, although in many instances older works are still useful for their exposition of well-established theories and practice.

Consulting available bibliographies, therefore, is the first essential step towards initiation into the literature of a subject. These compilations, consisting of systematically arranged descriptions of published (and sometimes unpublished) material, vary considerably, however. A few give almost universal coverage of subject, language, and period; these are the published catalogues of the great national libraries. Still comprehensive in subject coverage, but limited to the publications of a country, are the national bibliographies, for example, the *British National Bibliography* (see R. L. Collison, *Bibliographical Services Throughout the World*, 1950–9, Unesco, 1961). In between are the compilations that deal fairly exhaustively with all the publications in a particular language, for example, the *Cumulative Book Index*, a world list of books in the English language, published by H. W. Wilson, New York.

BRITISH MUSEUM. *General Catalogue of Printed Books*. London, Clewes, 1931–54. 51 volumes, A–Dezw. Photolithographical edition to 1955, vol. 52+, DF–. London, Trustees of the British Museum 1959–66. This author catalogue is one of the most valuable bibliographical tools

621.3012/9—Electrical Engineering. Special Materials

IMPERIAL CHEMICAL INDUSTRIES, LTD.
I.C.I. products for the electrical industry. London, Imperial Chemical Industries, gratis. 37cm. 25cm. Sd. (B56-4006)
Technical literature list as insert.

621.3017/8—METALS
621.3018—NON-FERROUS METALS
621.3018—ALUMINIUM

ALUMINIUM DEVELOPMENT ASSOCIATION
Aluminium in electrical engineering: an introductory survey. London, Aluminium Development Association, 4/6. May 1957. 72p. front, illus., tables. 28cm. Sd. (B57-9217)

BAILEY, John Cleaver
Aluminium in electrical engineering. London, Aluminium Development Association, gratis. Sep [1955]. 15p, illus., tables, bibliog. 28cm. Sd. (Aluminium Development Association. Reprints series—no.50) (B55-12599)
Reprinted from Metallurgia. Feb 1955.

621.3018[1]—ALUMINIUM. Essays

SYMPOSIUM ON ALUMINIUM AND ITS ALLOYS IN ELECTRICAL ENGINEERING, 1957, London
Aluminium and its alloys in electrical engineering; convened by the Aluminium Development Association and held at the Institution of Electrical Engineers, London, May 16 and 17, 1957. London, Aluminium Development Association, 20/-. 1957. 370p. illus., maps, tables, diagrs, bibliog. 22cm. Sd.

London, Technical P., 52/-. tables, diagrs. 22cm.

621.304—Essays on Electrical

BRITISH ELECTRICAL POWER Co
Proceedings. Winsley St., L
Power Convention.
7th: Brighton, 1955. Unpriced. plates(incl.port.), tables, diagrs. b
8th: Torquay, 1956. £1. 1956. maps, tables, diagrs. bibliog. 22.
Subsidiary subject: 625.[1]—Railw
9th: Eastbourne, 1957. £1. 195. plans, tables, diagrs. bibliog. 2

BRITISH THOMSON-HOUSTON Co
Rugby, 1956
Proceedings of the BTH thir engineering. Rugby, Britis [dMar 1957]. 154p. illus.(inc 27cm.

621.305—Periodicals on Electri

ELECTRIC Technology, U.S.S.R P., £6 (£20 per annum). M

Typewriter script. Four issues p Elektrichestvo translated into Eng

FIG. 1. *British National Bibliography.* (By permission of the Council of the British National Bibliography Ltd.)

available. The *Subject Index of Modern Works Acquired* has been regularly published since 1881.

UNITED STATES. LIBRARY OF CONGRESS. *A Catalog of Books Represented by Library of Congress Printed Cards issued to July* 31, 1942. Ann Arbor, Mich., Edwards, 1942–6. 167 volumes. Kept up to date by supplements. Since 1961 it has included titles reported by other American libraries, the first period covered being 1952–5. The subject index to books is published every 5 years, 1950–4 (20 vols.), 1955–9 (22 vols.), etc., supplemented by quarterly issues cumulating annually. (Now known as the *National Union Catalogue*.)

British National Bibliography, 1950 to date. London, Council of the British National Bibliography. (Fig. 1.) Entries are based on material received in the British Museum Copyright Office and they are arranged according to the Dewey Decimal Classification. Issued weekly, with quarterly and annual cumulations, with index. Cumulated indexes are published every 5 years, e.g. 1950–4, 1955–9, etc.

United States Catalog, 4th edn. New York, Wilson, 1928. Continued as the *Cumulative Book Index*, 1928 to date. New York, Wilson. (Fig. 2.) Issued monthly with subsequent cumulations, it lists practically every book in print in the United States as well as many books in English published in other countries. Books are arranged under author, subject, and title, in one alphabet.

Then there are the compilations of material by specific subjects which may be either comprehensive in scope and cover all forms of literature, regardless of language, or selective, with compilation for a particular readership. Within this range there are many variations.

Compilations also vary in the amount of detail given. Generally, sufficient information is given to help identification and purchase—author(s), title, publisher, date. Most useful are the bibliographies that provide commentary or annotations, giving

CUMULATIVE BOOK INDEX 227

Whitgift, J. A manual of demonstration technique. 12s 6d '65 Forbes publications, 92a Kensington High st, London, W. 8
See also
Electric current rectifiers
Electric machinery
Electric meters
Electric motors
Oscillators, Electric
Transducers

Testing

Conference on non-destructive testing in electrical engineering, 1961. Non-destructive testing in electrical engineering. pa £7 '62 Inst. of electrical eng.

Electric circuits

Abrahams, J. R. and Coverley, G. P. Signal flow analysis [with answers to questions] 17s 6d '65 Pergamon

Chance, B. and others, eds. Waveforms. pa **$3.25 '65 Dover**

Kron, G. Tensor analysis of networks. reprint 70s '65 MacDonald & co.

Marshall, J. L. Introduction to signal theory. $9 '65 Int. textbook

Mittleman, J. Circuit theory analysis. $11.25 '64 Hayden bk; 63s '65 Iliffe

Pearson, S. I. and Maler, G. J. Introductory circuit analysis. $10.75 (81s) '65 Wiley

Rogers, F. E. Topology and matrices in the **solution of networks. 45s '65 Iliffe**

Scott, R. E. Elements **of** linear circuits [with answers to exercises] $9.75 '65 Addison-Wesley

Siskind, C. S. Electrical circuits, direct and alternating current. 2d ed $8.75 (70s) '65 McGraw

Skilling, H. H. Electrical engineering circuts [with answers to sel. problems] 2d ed $10.75 '65 Wiley

Slurzberg, M. and Osterheld, W. Essentials of electricity-electronics. 3d ed $10.50 '65 McGraw
See also
Electric apparatus and appliances
Electric machinery
Electric power production
Electric railroads
Electric wiring
Radio
Telegraph

Apparatus and appliances

See Electric apparatus and appliances

Dictionaries and encyclopedias

Goedecke, W. Dictionary of electrical engineering, telecommunications and electronics. v 1 63s '65 Pitman

Juvenile literature

Sims, J. W. The boy electrician. 8th ed rev 18s '65 Harrap; **$4.25 Clarke, Irwin**

Materials

Conference on non-destructive testing in electrical engineering, 1961. Non-destructive testing in electrical engineering. pa £7 '62 Inst. of electrical eng.
See also
Semiconductors

Problems, exercises, etc.

Hamill, B. Problems in electrical engineering for technical students. 25s '65 Iliffe

Hinde, D. W. and Smith, K. M. Graded prob**lems for electrical engineers. 35s '65 Temple** press

Singer, B. B. Basic mathematics **for** electricity and electronics. 2d ed **$10.95; text ed** $7.50 '65 McGraw

Skilling, H. H. Electrical engineering circuits [with answers to sel. problems] 2d ed $10.75 '65 Wiley

FIG. 2. *Cumulative Book Index*. (By permission of the H. W. Wilson Co., New York.)

clues to extent and method of treatment and level of approach. Such treatment, of course, is characteristic of abstracting journals and progress reviews. It is also found in many of the guides to the literature of particular subjects.

A major difficulty is tracing the existence of bibliographies, particularly on technological subjects. They may be published as separates but more frequently they exist as appendixes to other material. Lists of books and articles for further reading are regular features in encyclopedias, handbooks, treatises, and textbooks. Scientific and technical reports and articles in periodicals normally include lists of other publications, particularly where they are used to substantiate the author's thesis.

Guides to Bibliographies

For the specialist who finds the broader subject guides lacking in sufficient detail, the most exhaustive compilation in existence is Theodore Besterman's *A World Bibliography of Bibliographies*, 4th edn., Lausanne, Societas Bibliographica, 1965, 4 volumes and an index. (Fig. 3.) Over 117,000 bibliographies are arranged under specific subject headings and, although dated for current technological application, can be of value for retrospective searches.

For current use the *Bibliographic Index* (Fig. 4), published in New York by H. W. Wilson, is invaluable. In addition to listing separately published bibliographies, it includes items located in books, periodicals, and serials. The *Index* is arranged alphabetically by specific subject. Published since 1938, this quarterly list has annual and larger cumulations.

Whilst not specifically guides to bibliographies, there are two excellent compilations covering all subject fields which include separately published bibliographies in addition to serving as introductions to all kinds of reference material:

WALFORD, A. J. (Editor). *Guide to Reference Material.* London, Library Association, 1959; Supplement 1963 (2nd edn., 1966-68 in 3 vols. Vol. 1: *Science & Technology*, 1966). (Fig. 5.)

ELECTRICITY AND MAGNETISM

1955. Электротехнический институт: Ленинград 1957. pp.148. [1750.]

[v. p. zhuze *and others*], Научная литература по полупроводниковым электронным приборам (детекторы и транзисторы). Библиография 1945–1955. Академия наук СССР: Институт полупроводников: Москва &c. 1959. pp.328. [3500.]

JUDY HAYES and ESTHER PEREIRA, Meissner effect, penetration depth, and residual magnetism in superconductors. California institute of technology: Jet propulsion laboratory: Astronautics information literature search (no.149): Pasadena 1959. pp.v.85.

SUPERCONDUCTIVITY 1959–1961. An annotated bibliography. Department of commerce: Office of technical services: [Washington 1961]. pp.iii.187. [355.]*

5. Electric generators and motors

ABRIDGMENTS of specifications. Class 35. Dyna-

ELECTRICITY AND MAGNETISM

SOME references to I.C. engine-electric road vehicles. Science library: Bibliographical series (no.729): 1954. ff.2. [41.]*

ELECTRIC motors — fractional horse power. Public library of South Australia: Research service: [Adelaide] 1958. ff.7. [111.]*

6. Electric lighting and heating

ABRIDGMENTS of specifications. Class 39. Electric lamps and furnaces. Patent office.

1855–1866. pp.v.10. [20.]
1867–1876. pp.v.12. [35.]
1877–1883. pp.xv.326. [1000.]
1884–1888. pp.ix.116. [350.]
1889–1892. pp.xii.162. [500.]
1893–1896. pp.xiv.186. [550.]
1897–1900. pp.xx.250. [750.]
1901–1904. pp.xx.334. [1000.]
1905–1908. pp.xxii.424. [1250.]
[*continued as:*]

FIG. 3. Besterman's *World Bibliography of Bibliographies*. (By permission of the Societas Bibliographica, Lausanne.)

WINCHELL, CONSTANCE M. *Guide to Reference Books*, 7th edn. Chicago, American Library Association, 1951. Three-year supplements; half-year supplements in *College and Research Libraries*. (New edition in the Press.)

More closely related to the literature of science and technology are the following bibliographies, published in the United States:

BURNS, ROBERT W. Literature resources for the sciences and technologies: a bibliographical guide. *Special Libraries*, **53**, 262–71. (1962.)

FLEMING, THOMAS P. *Guide to the Literature of Science*, 2nd edn. New York, Columbia School of Library Service, 1957.

JENKINS, FRANCES B. *Science Reference Sources*, 3rd edn. Champaign, Illinois, University of Illinois Library School, 1962.

SCHUTZE, GERTRUDE. *Bibliography of guides to the S–T–M* (Science–Technical–Medical) *Literature*, 1958–62; Supplement 1963.

Subject Guides

The most useful bibliographies, especially for readers approaching a subject for the first time, are the comprehensive surveys of all kinds of publication within a particular subject area. Some are descriptive and demonstrate method of use in finding information. Others are more modest and serve only as guides to the existence of material. Mathematics, physics, chemistry, nuclear energy, and metallurgy—all marginal subject fields—which cannot be ignored in electrical and electronic engineering —are adequately represented by descriptive guides. The publications covering electrical engineering specifically are mostly checklists.

Although a little dated now, a most useful publication is N. G. Parke, *Guide to the Literature of Mathematics and Physics*, including related works on engineering science, 2nd revised edn.,

40 BIBLIOGRAPHIC INDEX

ELECTRIC insulation. See Insulation (electric)
ELECTRIC lines
Bibliography of carrier, microwave, and wire-line literature applicable to power systems. Inst Elec & Electronics Eng Trans Power Apparatus & Systems 84:216-19 Mr '65
Magnusson, Philip Cooper. Transmission lines and wave propagation. (Allyn and Bacon ser. in electrical engineering) Allyn '65 incl bibliog

Carrier current control

See Carrier current control

Overhead

Hedman, D. E. Propagation on overhead transmission lines. Inst Elec & Electronics Eng Trans Power Apparatus & Systems 84:205, 211 Mr '65
ELECTRIC logging. See Petroleum—Well logging
ELECTRIC measurements
Mason, J. H. Discharge detection and measurements. Inst Elec Eng Proc 112:142 Jl '65
ELECTRIC motors, induction
Alger, Philip Langdon. Nature of induction machines. Gordon & Breach '65 incl bibliog
ELECTRIC plants. See Electric power plants
ELECTRIC power plants
Ostrava, Czechoslovak Republic (city). Státní vědecká knihovna. Elektrárny s plynovými turbinami; výběr literárních informací. (Publikace ser 2, no303) The library '61 19p
ELECTRIC power production
See also
Direct energy conversion
ELECTRIC properties
See also
Ceramic materials—Electric properties
ELECTRIC rectifiers

ELECTRONIC brains. See Artificial intelligence; Electronic calculating machines
ELECTRONIC calculating machines
Calingaert, Peter. Principles of computation. (Addison-Wesley ser. in computer science and information processing) Addison-Wesley '65 incl bibliog
Hertfordshire. County council. Technical information service. Select bibliography on computer applications in commerce and industry; comp. by C. R. Randall. 2d ed The service '65 64p
Stibic, Vladimír. Wege von der mechanisierung zur automatisierung der verwaltungsarbeit; übers. aus dem Tschechischen von Ludwig Brökl und Bruno Porsche. Verlag Die wirtschaft '62 p343-54
Thomas, Shirley. Computers: their history, present applications, and future. (Holt lib. of science, ser2, v 15) Holt '65 p 164-5
See also
Electronic data processing
Electronic digital computers

Print-out equipment

Chereau, L. Le système BBR et les applications des machines à calculer électroniques en imprimerie et en documentation. Bul Bibl France 9:104-7 Mr '65
ELECTRONIC circuits
Glasford, Glenn M. Linear analysis of electronic circuits. (Addison-Wesley ser. in electrical engineering) Addison-Wesley '65 incl bibliog
Lathrop, J. W. Semiconductor-network technology—1964. Inst Elec & Electronics Eng Proc 52:1444 D '64
Weimer, P. K. and others. Integrated circuits incorporating thin-film active and passive elements. Inst Elec & Electronics Eng Proc 52:1486 D '64
See also

FIG. 4. *Bibliographic Index.* (By permission of the H. W. Wilson Co., New York.)

New York, Dover Publications, 1958. Part 1, consisting of around 70 pages, places emphasis on the use of literature for reading, study, and making searches. The remainder of the book arranges over 5000 items under 120 main headings with further subdivision. Under Electronic and Electrical Engineering are the following sub-headings: handbooks and dictionaries; power and machinery; industrial; electronics; communications; high frequency and microwave radio; waveguides; etc. A few titles are annotated but most are not, so there is no guide to grading or selection.

A very useful complementary guide at college level, although limited by its date of publication, is R. H. Whitworth, *Physics Literature: reference manual*, Washington, Scarecrow Press, 1954.

Other guides in the same field include *Guide to the Literature of Physics*, published by the American Institute of Physics, 1962; *How to Find Out in Physics*, 1965; and J. E. Pemberton's *How to Find Out in Mathematics*, 1963, both published by the Pergamon Press.

A most useful publication, covering bibliographies, buyers guides, handbooks, data books, histories, dictionaries, textbooks, etc., is C. K. Moore and K. J. Spencer, *Electronics: a bibliographical guide*, London, Macdonald, 1961. (Fig. 6.) The major part of this book consists of periodical articles, books, reports, symposia papers, etc., mainly published between 1945 and 1959, arranged under detailed UDC headings and in chronological order. Each entry is annotated and includes information on the number of items covered in the list of references together with the inclusive dates. This book is one of a continuing series; a supplementary volume was published in 1965 and vol. 3 is in preparation. A supplementary volume on Electrical Engineering, compiled by D. E. Bagley, is also in the course of preparation.

Useful as checklists are:

CODLIN, E. M. (compiler). *Handlist of Basic Reference Material in Electrical and Electronic Engineering*, 2nd edn. London, Aslib, 1964.

RADIO COMMUNICATION

Bibliographies

621.396:016

"Abstracts and references", in *Electronic technology* (1960-62), *Wireless Engineer* (1957-59), *Electronic and radio engineer* (1924-56). London, Iliffe, 1924-62. Monthly.

As a supplement of abstracts to *Wireless engineer*, "Abstracts and references" was also issued separately. In 1955 it carried 3,902 informative and indicative abstracts, arranged in 18 sections, with U.D.C. nos. The annual author and subject indexes included a selected list of journals abstracted.

Monographs

621.396 (021)

BRITISH BROADCASTING CORPORATION. Engineering Division. **Monograph** No. 1-. London, B.B.C., [1955]-. 20s. p.a.

A series of monographs on technical subjects within the fields of television and sound broadcasting. Each describes work done by the Engineering Division of the B.B.C. and includes a survey of earlier work where appropriate. About six monographs are issued per annum.

Recent subjects include Stereophony (No. 52, 1964); Radiophonics in the B.B.C. (No. 51, 1963);

tables and data appended. The article "Electrostatics" occupies $3\frac{7}{8}$ columns; many cross-references. List of 13 principal contributors and main subjects covered. 800 clear illustrations and diagrams.

Dictionaries

621.396 (038)=00

CLASON, W. E., *comp.* **Elsevier's Dictionary of amplification, modulation, reception and transmission** in six languages: English/American, French, Spanish, Italian, Dutch and German. Amsterdam, London [etc.]. Elsevier, 1960. 804p. fl. 62.50; 120s.

2,924 terms dealing with amplification, modulation, reception and transmission of electromagnetic waves. The basic table is in English/American, with equivalents and reverse indexes in the other five languages. Repetition has been avoided, where possible, of terms correctly included in *Elsevier's Telecommunications dictionary* (see at 621.39 (038) = 00). Contains a large number of terms which have not found their way into existing dictionaries.

The *Supplement to the Elsevier dictionaries of electronics, nucleonics and telecommunication,* compiled by W. E. Clason (Amsterdam, London, etc., Elsevier, 1963. viii, 632p. 100s.), devotes 20% of its 2,503 additional terms to amplification, modulation, reception and transmission.

Fig. 5.   Walford's *Guide to Reference Material*, Vol. 1: *Science and Technology*, 2nd edn, 1966.
(By permission of the Library Association.)

SOMERVILLE, SHEILA. Bibliography of electrical engineering. *Library World*, September/October 1960, pp. 59–62, 85–91.

YOUNG, K. J. The Literature of Engineering. Part III. Electrical Engineering. *British Book News*, February 1961, pp. 83–88.

Guides to important interrelated subjects include:

AMERICAN CHEMICAL SOCIETY. *Searching the Chemical Literature*, 1961.

ANTHONY, L. J. *Sources of Information on Atomic Energy*. Pergamon Press, 1966.

BOTTLE, R. T. (Editor). *Use of the Chemical Literature*. Butterworths, 1962.

CRANE, E. J., *et al. Guide to the Literature of Chemistry*, 2nd edn., Wiley, 1957.

COLLEGE OF ENGINEERING, UNIVERSITY OF TEXAS. *Library Reference Manual for Engineering Students*. 1963.

GIBSON, E. B. and TAPIA, ELIZABETH, W. (Editors). *Guide to Metallurgical Information*. Special Library Association, 2nd edn., 1965.

UNITED KINGDOM. ATOMIC ENERGY AUTHORITY. *Sources of Information in Atomic Energy*. 3rd edn. HMSO, 1960 (AERE LIB/LI).

Special Libraries Publications

Because of their responsibilities to their scientific and techno-logical clientele, special libraries are far more comprehensive in their coverage of specific subject fields than the more general libraries. Their scope embraces all forms of material and is not limited to books or by language. Catalogues and other listings of the stock of these libraries, where they are available, therefore constitute excellent bibliographies.

The Engineering Societies Library in New York, which was established in 1913 through the merging of the long-established libraries of a dozen societies, including that of the American

c

46. MODULATION AND DEMODULATION (621.376)

46. MODULATION AND DEMODULATION (FREQUENCY CHANGERS, FREQUENCY TRANSLATORS, DETECTORS, MIXERS) (621.376)

1656. On conversion detectors. Strutt, M. J. O. *Proc. I.R.E.,* **22,** 8, Aug. 1934. 981–1008.

89 items
1926–1934.

In the main, the bibliog. covers the period Jan. 1930–Jan. 1934.

1657. A method of reducing disturbances in radio signalling by a system of frequency modulation. Armstrong, E. H. *Proc.I.R.E.,* **24,** 5, May 1936. 689–740.

13 items
1912–1934.

A pioneer paper.

1658. Evolution of frequency modulation. Armstrong, E. H. *Elect. Engng.,* **59,** 12, Dec. 1940. 485–493.

4 items
1922–1940.

A historical survey by a noted authority.

1659. Bibliography on frequency modulation. Rettenmeyer, F. X. Camden, N.J., Radio Corp. of America, 1942. 11 pp.

210 items
1922–1941.

Also published in *Radio,* No. 269, June 1942. 35–38 as *Radio bibliography: 2; frequency modulation.* Most of the items refer to world periodical literature.

1660. Frequency modulation. Hund, A. New York, McGraw-Hill, 1942. x, 375 pp.

178 items
1868–1942.

The bibliog. has the following sub-headings: wave propagation; antenna systems; noise; fundamentals and apparatus

FIG. 6.   Moore and Spencer's *Electronics: a bibliographical guide,* Vol. 1. (By permission of Macdonald & Co. (Publishers) Ltd.)

Institute of Electrical and Electronics Engineers, has a stock of over 180,000 volumes covering all branches of engineering, both archival and current. Its card catalogue, arranged according to a modified form of the UDC, has been reproduced in page form and is available from G. K. Hall of Boston, Massachusetts, in 13 volumes, including an index. It covers books, pamphlets, reports, bulletins, etc. Current accessions are listed in *Electrical Engineering*. The library also sends its new publications to *Engineering Index* to help its compilation. Consequently the *Index* in effect constitutes a ready-made published index to material available in the library.

The Institution of Electrical Engineers, in London, issued a more modest catalogue of its Lending Library in 1959, containing over 3600 items. It is in two sections, one for authors and the other for subjects arranged according to UDC. Updating is done by supplements, the third lists over 800 books added to the library during the period January 1959 and June 1964.

The Central Electricity Generating Board, at its London headquarters, maintains a large central library and an active information service. One of its most important publications, the *CEGB Digest* (Fig. 7), compiled by the Translations and Information Bulletins Section, is an abstracts bulletin covering English and foreign journals, conference papers, books, reports, recent CEGB bibliographies, and translations.

Also of value are the library and information publications issuing from the large and medium-sized firms. Apart from small works' libraries in different parts of the country, AEI maintains significant library and information services at its three main research centres at Rugby, Manchester, and Harlow. The Power Group Library, Manchester, issues a weekly technical news bulletin for design and research personnel, a weekly industrial digest of factory and workshop information for factory executives, and a monthly review covering automation and computation. The Rugby library compiles fortnightly an *Information Bulletin* covering semiconductors and dielectric materials and devices, electronic valves, microwave techniques, etc.

English Electric's largest library, at the Whetstone research centre, publishes a *Technical Literature Review, Recent Atomic Reports,* and a *Selected Contents List of Russian Journals,* all at weekly intervals. Nine other libraries within the group also

contaminated layer test at operating voltage a series of ratings is determined which makes it possible to make a comparative assessment of the different insulators. The possibility of designing insulation to fixed test values in accordance with the very widely differing stresses on insulators in operation has still to be explored. In addition to the continuously applied operating voltage, the insulator has also to withstand short-period over-voltages. Tests showed that rain appreciably reduces the withstand voltage in the case of switching voltages, especially with negative polarity.

Load, utilisation

273   STUDY OF THE SEASONAL VARIATION OF LOAD CURVES FOR WORKING-DAYS IN FRANCE, AND THE EVOLUTION OF THEIR SHAPES
D. Jung and G. Pioger
Economie Electrique, Vol. 39, No. 41 (1st Qr.) 1965, pp. 4-13; No. 42 (2nd Qr.) 1965, pp. 42-54; No. 43 (3rd Qr.) 1965, pp. 68-80 In French
        A method is examined for determining the seasonal variation of demand for each hour of the working day, and the modification with time of the shape of the daily load curve. Load curves for past years are reconstructed with corrections for random effects such as weather, strikes etc. Thus the seasonal variation of the hour at which peak demand occurs is examined, and effects such as the tending of the annual peak to fall more frequently in January are observed. An attempt is made to establish evolutionary laws making it possible to draw up future short-term load curves. The authors consider this to be the first study of its kind, and attribu⁺e its possibility to modern methods of calculation. Its disadvantages are the tediousness of the method, and the imperfect nature of the linear statistical adjust-ments used. Seventeen curves are illustrated.

Domestic applications

274   IMPROVED AUTOMATIC CHARGING AND CONTROL UNIT FOR ELECTRIC THERMAL STORAGE HEATERS OF ALL TYPES
H. Freundlieb
Elektrowärme, Vol. 24, No. 1, pp. 13-19 (Jan. 1966) In German

FIG. 7.   *CEGB Information Services Digest.*   (By permission of the Central Electricity Generating Board.)

compile bulletins. Working in a more specialized field is the IBM library, at Hursley Park, Winchester, which produces by computer techniques a fortnightly current-awareness bulletin.

Similar activities are reported by electrical firms in the United States, for example, General Electric, Consolidated Edison, and the Bell Telephone Laboratories. The last has an extensive network of company libraries and the largest industrial research library in the USA, handles over 30,000 requests each year for technical reports, and stocks over 56,000 volumes and more than 4700 periodicals. It has an impressive bibliographical output. There is a fortnightly *Current Technical Papers*, covering some 600 scientific and engineering journals and totalling 30,000 items per year; a fortnightly *Current Technical Reports*, covering over 9000 documents each year; and a *Library Bulletin*, which announces new books and lists all bibliographies and translations recently prepared by the information service. A monthly *Computer Abstract Bulletin* is also available.

Of wider subject scope, but with good representation of electrical and electronic engineering, are the libraries of the Science Museum and the Patent Office, in London. The Science Library holds the more important scientific and technical publications, books, and periodicals; consequently its weekly accessions list and subject bibliographies are very useful. The latter are produced upon request, the total number having reached almost 800. A list of these currently available can be obtained free. The Patent Office Library, which is building up its stock in preparation for the role of National Reference Library of Science and Invention, publishes a list of its additions in the Patent Office *Official Journal*. (On 1 April 1966 this library became part of the British Museum, Dept. of Printed Books.)

Using Libraries

Library provision may vary according to type of reader—student, craftsman, technician, engineer, scientist, statistician, or administrator—but in all cases facilities for reference and loan exist, even though they may vary by degrees in the excellence of the service provided. Some will use the library of a college, university, research organization, society, or industrial establishment, but for many the public library will be the mainstay. Linked as they are, however, through the various systems of inter-library co-operation, there is no reason to assume that the various kinds of material discussed in this book cannot be located eventually. Even the special libraries serving the scientist, technologist, and management cannot pretend to be completely self-sufficient; frequently they also have to turn to other libraries for assistance.

Ideally the public library should serve as the research library for small firms in the locality, the place where technical workers can go to keep up to date with their subject and where answers to many inquiries can be found. Many of the larger municipal libraries, particularly in industrial areas, carry good stocks of scientific, technical, and commercial materials. The county library systems, too, with industrial localities within their boundaries, are developing similar services.

Manchester, an example of a large city system, has separate technical and commercial libraries, and another library for patents and microtext. The technical library is open from 9 a.m. to 9 p.m. and caters for all levels. Its acquisition policy is to purchase a copy of every scientific and technical textbook published in Great Britain except for those of elementary or trivial standard. It also acquires a large percentage of USA output and a representative selection of the more important works in principal European languages. It also receives regularly over 1200 periodicals (including almost 300 indexing and abstracting journals) and enjoys close co-operation with special libraries in the neighbourhood, some of which are concerned with electrical engineering, atomic energy, and television. The commercial library stocks 3750 different directories and receives 1150 periodicals. Lewisham, in London, typifying a smaller public library system, has a separate library for science and technology and takes 450 technical and trade journals, including 75 abstracting and indexing services. For local industry it produces monthly a

Technical Periodical Review, Part B covering electrical engineering.

National Libraries

Every public library in Great Britain, and a number of academic and special libraries, is linked through regional bureaux to the National Central Library which maintains union catalogues of library holdings. In addition, there are the various schemes of local co-operation between libraries of different kinds, mainly centred on the local public library. Basic aims are to pool resources and maintain union catalogues. Such schemes operate in Birmingham, Bradford, West London, Hampshire, Hertfordshire, Huddersfield, Hull, Liverpool, Leeds, Nottingham, Sheffield, and Tyneside.

Supplementing internal library resources and the regional system of inter-library co-operation is the service offered by the National Lending Library for Science and Technology (Department of Education and Science) at Boston Spa, in Yorkshire. To support its aim to cover all the literature of value required by the scientist, technologist, and doctor, the NLL subscribes to about 23,000 periodical titles and serials and holds the best collection of Russian serials in western Europe. English language, Russian and French books are systematically ordered, and approximately 25,000 scientific and technical reports (mostly from the USA) are received each year. It is also attempting comprehensive coverage of recent conference proceedings, and sponsors and collects translations. Its 24-hour postal loans service operates through approved libraries in industry, government, local authorities, colleges, and universities. Individuals and organizations not eligible as direct users can borrow from the NLL by using "local agents"—public and technical college libraries equipped with essential scientific and technical bibliographies. (A full account of the National Lending Library, the Patent Office Library, and the special library set-up in the United Kingdom is given in J. Burkett's *Special Libraries and Information*

Services in the United Kingdom, 2nd edn., London, Library Association, 1965.) The NLL has recently added social sciences to its scope.

Another very important library for the technologist, but for reference only, is the Patent Office Library, Chancery Lane, London, planned to become the National Reference Library of Science and Invention (now under the administration of the British Museum). With a current stock of over 400,000 volumes covering very much the same scope as the National Lending Library, it is building up to an ultimate total of 1 million volumes. Many of its 9000 current periodicals (the total may eventually equal the NLL's) are filed for long periods. An additional facility is the patents collection; British publications accumulate at the rate of 30,000 a year, foreign patent specifications and applications at 300,000 a year. The Patent Office operates both a 24-hour postal service and a while-you-wait service for photocopies.

The Science Museum Library, which is also fairly comprehensive in its holdings of books and periodicals (working in close association with the National Lending Library), continues to operate its postal photocopying service.

Another important development for the technical man is the introduction by the Department of Scientific and Industrial Research (now taken over by the Ministry of Technology) of Industrial Liaison Centres. Staffed by full-time industrial liaison officers, they are normally located at colleges of advanced technology or technical colleges and their task is to stimulate industry to make greater use of scientific and technical knowledge, backed by both local public library resources and the special resources of the college. Fifty centres are planned by 1967.

Special Library Resources

The technologist and others users of electrical engineering information may wish to have access to libraries, special collections, and other sources of information further afield than his own local library. Bona-fide inquirers are rarely turned away by special libraries, even those maintained by industrial firms.

The following publications, therefore, may prove to be of value:

Aslib Directory. London, 1957. 2 volumes. Over 3300 libraries are arranged geographically, with an index to the subject specialities. (New edition in preparation.)

American Library Directory. New York, Bowker, 25th edn., 1966. Covers over 15,000 libraries in the USA and Canada.

Specialized Science Information Services in the United States. National Science Foundation, 1961.

Guide to Special Book Collections and Subject Emphases, etc., 2nd edn., Bowker, 1961. Covers university, college, public, and special libraries in the United States and Canada; its arrangement is alphabetical by subject. A companion volume *Subject Collections in European Libraries* was published in 1965.

Directory of Special Libraries and Information Centres (edited by A. T. Kruzas). Detroit, Gale Research Co., 1963. Gives brief details of holdings, services and staff in 10,000 libraries in the United States and Canada, with a subject index.

Other guides to sources of information can be located in A. J. Walford's *Guide to Reference Material.*

Classification of Electrical Engineering

Although there is a trend towards punched-card indexing and computer-sorting of information, bibliographical schemes of classification are firmly established in most libraries for the recording and systematic arrangement of information appearing in different forms, even if it is not shelved together. In spite of certain faults, the scheme most likely to be met in public libraries is the Dewey Decimal Classification, now in its 17th edition. It is also used by the *British National Bibliography.* Basically the DDC distributes the whole of human knowledge into nine main clases and identifies each with a three-figure notation, e.g.:

| 100 | Philosophy | 500 | Pure Science |
| 600 | Applied Science. | | |

The remaining class is Generalia, 000. Each main class is broken down into ten subdivisions:

    600   Applied Sciences. Technology
    610   Medicine
    620   Engineering
    630   Agriculture.

Further divisions are made with the increased specificity of subject:

621	Mechanical Engineering
621.3	Electrical Engineering
621.38	Electronic and Electric Communication Engineering
621.384	Radio Communication Engineering
621.384 51	Microwave Radio

The scheme used in many specialist electrical engineering information centres, however, is the Universal Decimal Classification, a descendant of the Dewey Classification. It was also used for the arrangement of abstracts in *Electrical Engineering Abstracts*, edited and published by the Institution of Electrical Engineers; *Technisches Zentralblatt: Elektrotechnik*, compiled by the Deutsche Akademie der Wissenschaften; and *VDE-Schnellberichte* (Electrotechnik), a weekly indexing service.

Both schemes have many similarities, particularly in the main classes and subdivisions, but the UDC, because of its technological bias, goes into very much greater detail and has many additional topics not covered by Dewey.

> Microwave Radio Systems in UDC is 621.396.24
> Communication Engineering which in Dewey is contained by the subdivisions 621.382–621.389, here receives a shorter notation: 621.39, after which the breakdown is very specific, e.g.:
> 621.396.611.31 Radio Communication—Circuits—Oscil-atory—Coupled—Loose.

Because UDC is used by the well-established abstracting services in electrical engineering and by so many special libraries, its main subdivisions will be followed in this guide. Any variations from Dewey should not worry unduly the public library user.

References

Guide to the Universal Decimal Classification (UDC). British Standards Institution, BS 1000C: 1963.

UDC, vol. 4, part 2: *Class* 621.3 *Electrical Engineering*. British Standards Institution, BS 1000: vol. 4, part 2.

Questions

1. Under the heading for Electrical Engineering in general, examine *BNB* for the past 5 years and estimate the ratio of government publications to publications from all other sources.

2. Select six bibliographies listed in Besterman relevant to your subject field and published within the same period of 10 years. Note the number of references cited more than once and also the span of years between the first and latest citations.

3. Discuss the value to electric engineers of guides to the literature in associated subject areas using specific works as examples.

4. Using appropriate reference tools, list special libraries in the United Kingdom closely connected with electrical engineering and arrange them in regional order.

5. Choose ten different aspects within the field of electrical engineering and compare their treatment in the Decimal Classification and in the Universal Decimal Classification.

CHAPTER 3

Acquisition and Selection

THE profusion of material currently issuing from so many different publishing bodies, combined with the limitations of space and purchasing power, makes careful selection a necessity. Duplication often occurs in the same field and a choice has to be made from two or more similar books published by different companies. Before we consider the criteria to be adopted for book selection, however, it is necessary to look at current bibliographies to determine the availability of older established works, what has recently appeared, and finally, titles planned for publication in the near future.

Books in Print

After systematically searching the different bibliographies for all the literature in a particular subject area, the next step is to determine whether or not the various items listed are currently available for purchase. Even in a rapidly changing technology such as electrical engineering, where frequent new editions appear of standard books, some of the older authoritative works covering fundamental theories are still required for teaching and reference purposes. It is necessary, therefore, to determine the availability of reprints, some of which are now appearing in paperback form, thus making them more accessible to the individual with limited funds. The guides to British and American publications currently available which are listed below can be seen in most public libraries.

32

US Publications

Publishers' Trade List Annual. New York, Bowker. A collection of publishers' catalogues arranged alphabetically by the name of the publisher.

Books in Print. New York, Bowker. Annual. Arranged under authors, titles and series.

Subject Guide to Books in Print. New York, Bowker, Annual. Serves as an index to the *Publishers' Trade List Annual.*

ORTON, R. M. *Catalogue of Reprints in Series*, 19th edn. Scarecrow Press, 1961. A guide to reprint editions of certain works currently available.

UK Publications

British Books in Print. London, Whitaker, 1966. Records the in-print titles of 1889 publishers; by author in volume 1, by title in volume 2. Previously issued as *The Reference Catalogue of Current Literature.*

Technical Books in Print. London, Whitaker. Annual. First published in 1964, this is a catalogue of nearly 9000 titles in print and on sale in Great Britain at November 1964. Headings are arranged approximately according to the Dewey Classification.

Catalogue of Lewis's Medical, Scientific and Technical Lending Library. London, H. K. Lewis & Co. Ltd., 1965. Supplementary lists are issued every 2 months. Although limited in bibliographical detail (e.g. the omission of publishers' names), it contains most of the significant British and American publications readily available for loan, by subscription, or for purchase. Subject catalogues are also issued from time to time, including one for Electrical Engineering.

Other booksellers such as Blackwell of Oxford and Heffer of Cambridge issue similar subject lists from time to time.

Paperback Editions
> *Paperbound Books in Print*. New York, Bowker. Each issue,
> which appears quarterly, including a subject index.
> *Paperbacks in Print*. London, Whitaker. Half-yearly.

Current Publications

The two most authoritative compilations for English language publications, the *Cumulative Book Index* and *British National Bibliography*, were described in Chapter 2. They serve both for retrospective and current searches. *CBI* is complemented by *Publishers' Weekly*, New York, and the *American Book Publishing Record* (Bowker) which is a helpful cumulation of books listed in *Publishers' Weekly* over the past 4 to 5 weeks, arranged in classified order with an author and title index.

In addition to *BNB*'s weekly issues, other publications listing very recent British titles include the weekly *Bookseller* (Whitaker), cumulating quarterly and yearly into Whitaker's *Cumulative Book List*, and the weekly *British Books* with its annual cumulation the *English Catalogue*.

All of these compilations, of course, are comprehensive in their subject coverage, but they are limited in the kinds of publication they include. Conference papers, patents, trade literature, periodical articles, and a great number of research reports are excluded. It is highly desirable, therefore, to have access to the accessions lists of libraries specializing in the field. Up to a point, the fact that material has been considered worthwhile for acquisition by a special library can be considered a criterion for selection. It is also common practice to obtain scientific and technical books on approval and to rely on the advice of specialists for help in making a final decision for retention.

Aids to Selection

The reputation of publishers, authors, special series, and series editors is an important criterion in the selection of material. The continuation and revision of a particular book through a number of editions is usually another reliable indication.

The catalogues available from publishers normally cover all books currently in print, all books available within one or more subject areas, and advance notice of publications in the press. McGraw-Hill, Methuen, Chapman & Hall, Spon, and others, issue annually a list for electrical engineering. In other instances, such as Blackie, engineering is combined with books on science. Most of these catalogues are quite informative and give details of level of treatment, the author's qualifications, and a list of contents.

Identification of a publication within a particular series can be very helpful if the reader is already familiar with other titles in the same series. The pattern of treatment, level of approach, and the suitability of the author, are usually similar throughout.

Electrical Engineering Series

ACADEMIC PRESS. Methods of Experimental Physics series.

ADDISON-WESLEY. Computer Science and Information Processing series.

BLACKIE. The Student's Physics series, and the Electronic User Series.

BRITISH BROADCASTING CORPORATION. Engineering Monographs.

CHAPMAN & HALL. Modern Electrical Studies, Monographs on Electrical Engineering, Advanced Engineering Textbooks (a series recommended for publication by technologists of Associated Electrical Industries Ltd.), Monographs for Students—published on behalf of the Institute of Physics and the Physical Society.

CLEAVER-HUME. Electrical series, Philips Technical Library.

FOULSHAM'S Basic Electricity/Electronics series.

ILIFFE. Radio Servicing series, Young Engineer series, Philips Paper Backs.

LONGMANS. Electrical Engineering series.

McGRAW-HILL. Electrical and Electronic Engineering series, Westinghouse Engineering Books for Industry, Massachusetts Institute of Technology Radiation Laboratory series, Control Systems Engineering series, Information Processing and Computers series.

METHUEN. Monographs on Physical Subjects.

NEWNES. Practical Handbook series.

PERGAMON PRESS. The Commonwealth and International Library of Science, Technology, Engineering and Liberal Studies. International Series of Monographs on Electromagnetic Waves.

PITMAN. Radio and Electronic Components series.

PRENTICE-HALL. Electrical Engineering series.

VAN NOSTRAND. Electronics and Communications series, Bell Telephone Laboratory series, Marconi series.

Annotated Guides

Some readers may prefer to rely on their own judgement for selection, but for those not possessing the specialist knowledge selective lists from authoritative sources are invaluable. *The Aslib Book List*, published monthly, is a good example of this type of bibliography. It is a list of recommended scientific and technical books, compiled by subject specialists, arranged according to the Universal Decimal Classification. Where necessary, items carry annotations, but each entry is graded by the letters A to D to indicate elementary, intermediate, and advanced levels of treatment, and reference works.

Another very useful publication by Bowker which includes analyses of contents and descriptive or critical annotations is *American Scientific Books* (annual). It cumulates all the relevant books published in *American Book Publishing Record*, arranging entries by Dewey. Also from the United States is the excellent *New Technical Books* issued monthly by the New York Public Library. With reviews by competent staff, it is a selective listing arranged according to the Dewey Decimal Classification scheme. A new publication is *Sci-Tech Book Profiles* (monthly, Bowker).

Book Reviews

Well-established journals receive copies of all new books in their field and it is usually the policy of the editors to select the more outstanding titles and commission experts to write reviews. If the job of selection is well done, mediocre books should not appear. Unfortunately there is often a time-lag between publication date and the appearance of the review.

Apart from the well-known commercially published periodicals, book reviews regularly appear in the periodical publications of the two outstanding societies in the field: the Institute of Electric and Electronic Engineers in the USA and the Institution of Electrical Engineers in London. An average of ten medium-length reviews appear in each issue of the bi-monthly *Electricity*, published by the Electricity Council. In Europe, other useful sources of reviews are the *Bulletin de la Société Française des Électriciens* (monthly) and *L'Elettrotecnica* (monthly) published by the Associazone Elettrotecnica ed Elettronica Italiana. A good example of a reviewing journal in a specialized field is *Solid-state Electronics*, published monthly by Pergamon Press and carrying approximately ten signed reviews each issue, some of which are quite long.

There are two periodical publications devoted solely to reviews of books in technology: *Technical Book Review*, published monthly by Directory Publications Ltd., London, and the *Technical Book Review Index*, published monthly (except July and August) by the Special Libraries Association and compiled in the Carnegie Library of Pittsburgh.

The former carries long evaluative reviews by specialists, in addition to notes on other books received. The purpose of the *Index* is primarily to identify reviews in current scientific, technical and trade journals, and help evaluation by quoting from the reviews selected. Over 100 items are covered in each issue and they are arranged alphabetically by author.

Questions

1. What are the limitations to comprehensive coverage in using current national bibliographies? Give examples.

2. Examine the book reviews in a select number of current electrical periodicals and comment on (a) timeliness, (b) authority of the reviewer, (c) bias, if any, (d) level of reader intended.

3. Choose an important publisher's series within your subject field and write notes on (a) scope, (b) authority of editors and authors, (c) level of treatment, (d) standard of presentation.

CHAPTER 4

Handbooks, Treatises, Textbooks, Standards and Regulations
UDC 621.3(02)

VERY few scientists and technologists can carry in their heads a great number of theories, precise details, working principles, standards, formulae, physical and mechanical properties, and so on. There is a constant need, therefore, for publications which contain concise up-to-date and lucid accounts of every important facet of specific areas of electrical and electronic engineering, arranged systematically. The encyclopedia is useful from this point of view for quick reference, but it is limited for professional use by its arrangement which distributes closely related headings throughout an alphabetical sequence.

The conventional procedure for information searchers follows a definite pattern starting with handbooks which survey fairly broad subject areas and arrange data in a compact and convenient form. So far as accuracy is concerned the handbooks of reliable technical publishers normally leave little room for criticism. Many carry the name of a particular editor of repute for years, and the compilation is supported usually by a large number of specialists. Unless there is evidence to the contrary one must assume that these named contributors have done the work themselves and not delegated it to juniors. The date of a publication needs to be checked, and it is useful to note the frequency of new editions. Some publishers do not issue a revised edition, however, until new developments have been proven sound and have been absorbed as part of the common store of knowledge.

Another feature to be checked is the scope of coverage and subjects that have been omitted. Some sections of electrical engineering and electronic engineering have developed so extensively that they cannot be dealt with satisfactorily in one volume and often justify separate handbooks.

If an inquiry is not satisfied adequately through the handbook, the next step is to consult a treatise on the subject. Treatises are scholarly and advanced works usually based on the world's outstanding theory and practice. They are systematically arranged and they are not intended for quick reference. Although authoritative in themselves they refer to other authorities where original work has been discussed. The treatise, therefore, is a good source for bibliographies.

Textbooks are not basically ready reference books either, but they can often be used for this purpose although, like the more advanced treatise, they are intended for consecutive reading. They develop a theme in a branch of knowledge as opposed to supplying precise information on a more limited topic, the province of the monograph. Often textbooks may be the only source of reliable material and, because of the varying grades of text to suit different degrees of education, they may be preferred by readers approaching a subject for the first time. They are not normally very good sources of bibliographies.

Handbooks

An essential reference book in the closely related field of physics is the *American Institute of Physics Handbook* (Fig. 8). The 2nd edn., published in 1963 by McGraw-Hill, has reflected current trends by adding special chapters on analogue and digital computers, solid-state physics, etc. Over 100 contributors are responsible for the highly informative and critical data covered. Section 5 is an extensive treatment of electricity and magnetism, including electrical power practices and electrochemical information. Magnetic Properties of Materials is given over 270 pages covering symbols, formulae, tables of properties, and constants. Each section has good bibliographies.

TABLE 5h-1. FRACTIONAL-HORSEPOWER MOTOR CHARACTERISTICS

Type of motor	Hp range	Speed data: Rated speed (for 60 cps a-c or d-c only)	Speed data: Speed characteristics	Speed control	Rated voltage	Torque (% of full load): Starting	Torque (% of full load): Max	Reversible	Radio interference	Approx price comparison, %	Application
A-C:											
Single phase:											
Shaded pole....	0.001–1/20	800, 1,050, 1,550, 3,000	Almost constant	None	115	30–50	Less than 175	No	No	60	Used for low-starting-torque loads. Typical applications include desk fans, phonograph turntables, and toys
Split phase.....	1/20–1/3	850, 1,140, 1,725, 3,450	Almost constant	None	115, 230	90–275	185–300	Yes, change connections	No	100	For applications with low- or medium-starting-torque loads, such as washing machines, light machine tools, oil burners, ironers, office appliances
Capacitor start..	1/8–3/4	850, 1,140, 1,725, 3,450	Almost constant	None	115, 230	250–425	225–500	Yes, change connections	No	125	A high-starting-torque motor, used for refrigerators, air conditioning, conveyors, compressors
Permanent-split capacitor	1/20–3/4	825, 1,075, 1,625, 3,250	Almost constant	None	115, 230	50–100	150–225	Yes, change connections	No	140	A medium-starting-torque motor. Used for fans blowers, tool grinders
Synchronous....	0.001–1/3	900, 1,200, 1,800, 3,600 and many speeds below 900	Absolutely constant	None	115	50–250	175–225	Yes, change connections	No	400	For applications where a constant speed is needed, such as timing devices, indicating instruments, testing equipment for speedometers, teleprinters, facsimile printers
Polyphase, squirrel cage	1/8–3/4	850, 1,140, 1,725, 3,450	Almost constant	None	110, 208, 220, 440	200–350	200–350	Yes, change connections	No	175	For practically all applications where a polyphase supply is available. Characteristics are similar to those of the capacitor-start motor
D-C, shunt wound...	1/20–3/4	850, 1,140, 1,725, 3,450	Almost constant Varies with load	Field resistance Armature resistance	115, 230	Above 400 %	....	Yes, change connections	Yes	200	For practically all applications where a d-c supply is available. May be used where an adjustable speed is required
A-C or d-c, series universal	1/20–3/4	1,500–12,000	Varies with load	Resistance	115, 230	Above 400 %	....	Yes, change connections	Yes	150	Used where a high-speed motor is required, such as vacuum cleaners, electric typewriters, electric drills. Speed may be adjusted, making it useful for sewing machines and food mixers

FIG. 8. *American Institute of Physics Handbook*, 2nd edn., 1963. (Copyright McGraw-Hill Book Co. Inc. Used by permission.)

An outstanding reference book for students and practising engineers concerned with electrical engineering is Archer E. Knowlton's *Standard Handbook for Electrical Engineers*, now in its 9th edn. (McGraw-Hill, 1957; 1st edn. 1907). It forms a handy reference compilation of practical usable data from all fields of electrical engineering, together with the most frequently required fundamental theory, units, and systems of measurement. The 26 chapters of the book are the work of over 100 collaborators; each chapter carrying a bibliography.

Another useful reference book, but presented without advanced mathematics and intended for practical electrical workers, is *Croft's American Electricians' Handbook*, 8th edn. edited by Clifford C. Carr, 1961 (McGraw-Hill). It is designed for the intelligent selection, installation, maintenance, and operation of electrical equipment and covers the properties and splicing of conductors, circuits and calculations, general electrical equipment and batteries, transformers, electron tubes and circuits, generators and motors, outside distribution, interior wiring, electrical lighting, and wiring tables.

An excellent British publication, first published in 1945 and now in an 11th edition, is *The Electrical Engineer's Reference Book*, edited by M. G. Say (London, George Newnes, 1964) (Fig. 9). This standard work of reference, divided into 33 sections with contributions from over 70 specialist contributors, covers modern theory, practice, and equipment, and the most recent developments in all branches of electrical engineering. Examples of relatively new topics included are: magneto-hydrodynamics, fuel cells, irradiation effect on materials, printed circuits and encapsulation, electronic control methods, silicon-controlled rectifiers, computers, and automatic warning systems for train control. Other chapters cover education and training; periodicals and standards; and electricity rules, regulations, and supply data.

Fig. 9 (*opposite*). Say's *Electrical Engineer's Reference Book*, 1964. (By permission of George Newnes Ltd.)

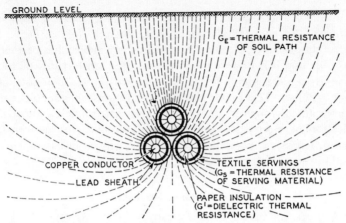

FIG. 14.—HEAT FLOW PATH FOR A TREFOIL GROUP OF SINGLE-CORE CABLES LAID DIRECT.

Three main factors decide the safe continuous current a cable will carry: (1) The maximum permissible temperature at which its components may be operated with a reasonable factor of safety. (2) The heat-dissipating properties. (3) The installation conditions and the ambient conditions obtaining.

Heat Flow from a Cable.

The current carried by a copper conductor raises its temperature until equilibrium is established, and the heat generated is equal to the heat dissipated through the insulation, metal sheath, cable servings and finally into the surrounding earth or air. Fig. 14 illustrates the heat flow field of three single-core cables laid direct in the ground; and Fig. 15 (b) that resulting from load current carried by a three-core " belted " cable.

It will be seen from Fig. 15 (b) that the three copper conductors, assumed at the same temperature, are in effect one thermal pole. The earth's surface represents the other pole, so that the total temperature-difference is given by the conductor ambient temperature drop.

From the conductor the heat flows outwards through three parallel paths,

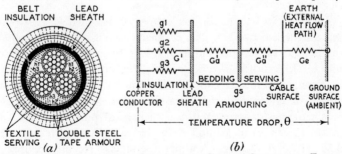

FIG. 15.—HEAT FLOW RESULTING FROM LOAD CURRENT CARRIED BY A THREE-CORE " BELTED " CABLE.

Mr. Say is also responsible for the *Electrical Engineering Design Manual*, 3rd edn. (Chapman & Hall, 1962).

As stated earlier, electrical engineering as a subject has become so wide that it is now very difficult to cover satisfactorily all the important data and information required by technologists in one volume. The trend, therefore, is towards handbooks for important divisions of the broader field, for example industrial electronics, electronics engineering, electronics measurements, radio, television, computers, etc. These will be discussed later within the appropriate chapters.

Treatises and Textbooks

A great number of books already exist in this category and others are being added every year, the total being far too numerous for listing in a guide of this nature. Many levels of readership are represented in this output; therefore to make such a list useful comments would be necessary related to the potential reader's background and requirement. As an indication, however, of the range of material available, a selection of recognized standard works is given below. Others on more specific subjects are included in the appropriate chapters. Because of the changing pattern of the various syllabuses to meet current theoretical and technological requirements, it is important to carefully check editions and read the authors' prefaces.

Degree Requirements

Basic works for the British degree course include *Electricity and Magnetism* by B. I. and B. Bleaney, first published in 1957 and issued as a second edition in 1965 (Oxford University Press), and C. J. Smith's *Electricity and Magnetism*, 3rd edn., 1963 (London, Arnold, 1st edn., 1954). Smith's book is an account of the fundamental parts of classical electricity and magnetism, both from an experimental and theoretical point of view, and covers rather more ground than that usually required for the B.Sc. General Degree. Another useful text recently revised is *Electricity and Magnetism* by J. H. Fewkes and John Yarwood,

2nd edn., 1965 (London, University Tutorial Press). Although it covers the requirements for the B.Sc. General Degree, Part 1 of London University's B.Sc. Special Physics Degree, and Part 1 of the Cambridge Natural Sciences Tripos, in some cases, for example electronics and radio communication, sections have been added which are somewhat outside immediate degree requirements.

Suitable texts for students of applied electricity include H. Cotton's *Advanced Electrical Technology*, 1966 (Pitman), and the same author's *Applied Electricity* 6th edn., 1966 (Macmillan) covering Part I of the B.Sc. (Engineering) Degree and the appropriate examinations of the Institution of Electrical Engineering and the national certificates and diplomas. At the same level is *Fundamentals of Electrical Engineering* by E. Hughes, 2nd edn. (Longmans, 1963) and A. T. Starr's *Applied Electricity* (Pitman, 1957).

Other first-year degree texts include S. J. Kowalski's *Introduction to Electrotechnology* (Chapman & Hall, 2nd edn., 1966) and A. W. Hirst's *Electricity and Magnetism for Engineering Students*, 3rd edn., 1959 (Blackie). Another book by Hirst that covers the electrical engineering requirements of the London B.Sc. (Engineering) Degree, Parts 2 and 3, is *Applied Electricity*, now in its 4th edition (Blackie, 1966).

A good standard work that combines theory with practice, written for B.Sc. and diploma requirements, is Philip Kemp's *Alternating Current Electrical Engineering*, 10th edn. (Macmillan, 1963). Since it was first published in 1918 this book has been regularly revised and reached its 9th edition in 1958. An American work covering the same ground and beyond is Chester L. Dawes' *Industrial Electricity* in 2 volumes (McGraw-Hill). Volume 1, covering *Direct Currents*, appeared in a 3rd edition in 1956; vol. 2 on *Alternating Currents*, also in the 3rd edition, was published in 1960.

National Certificates

In addition to titles already mentioned, two recently revised books for Ordinary National Certificate (ONC) requirements are *Principles of Electricity* by A. Morley and E. Hughes, 2nd edn., 1964 (Longmans) and its sequal *Electrical Technology*, 2nd edn., 1963 (Longmans). The former has been revised to cater for the new ONC requirements of the 2-year senior course and covers the whole of the second year in electrical engineering science and most of the second-year syllabus. The latter was intended for the third year of ONC, the first year of the engineering degree course and the intermediate examinations of the City and Guilds of the London Institute.

American Textbooks

A number of books are available at American university course level based on practical lecturing experience. *Principles and Practice of Electrical Engineering* by A. Gray and G. A. Wallace (McGraw-Hill, 1962) and now in an 8th edition, for example, has been based on lectures given to senior civil, mechanical, and mining students at the McGill University. It covers the broad aspects of circuit theory, electronics, semiconductors, magnetic amplifiers, power equipment, transformers, and illumination.

At a similar level, and based on lectures given at the Cornell University, is *Electrical Engineering: theory and practice* by W. H. Erickson and N. H. Bryant, 2nd edn. (New York, Wiley).

Two practical introductory texts are *Basic Electrical Engineering* (2nd edn., 1957) and *Fundamentals of Electrical and Electronic Engineering* (1964), both by A. E. Fitzgerald and D. E. Higginbotham, and published by McGraw-Hill. The former covers circuit theory, machinery, industrial electronics and measurements, and feedback-control systems; the latter is intended for the engineering technician.

Standards, Specifications and Regulations

In electrical engineering, standards are of importance in three broad categories: scientific standards as units of measurement; technical standards as evaluations of quality, performance, or dimensions; and standard terminology, an important aid to correct communications between engineers and others.

The basic scientific electrical standards are the ohm and the volt now measured by what is known as the absolute system which was adopted from 1 January 1948 by international agreement. These standards are based on the metre, the kilogram, and the second; national institutions in each country are responsible for the maintenance of accurate secondary standards. In the United Kingdom, the National Physical Laboratory, and in the United States of America, the National Bureau of Standards, are charged with this duty.

The National Physical Laboratory produces a series of *Units and Standards of Measurement Employed at the National Physical Laboratory* of which No. 3 is *Electricity: current, voltage, resistance, power, energy, inductance, capacity, frequency, etc.* (1962). The National Bureau of Standards publishes various relevant documents: a useful guide is "Electrical Standards" by F. K. Harris in the *American Institute of Physics Handbook* (2nd edn., 1963), pp. 5. 96–106.

Guides to international scientific standards include *International and Metric Units of Measurement* by Marvin H. Green (1962); Elsevier's *Lexicon of International and National Units*, compiled by W. E. Clason (1964); and another useful work is *A Dictionary of Scientific Units* by H. G. Jerrard and D. B. McNeill (1964). National Bureau of Standards Miscellaneous Publication 260–4, February 1965, *Standard Reference Materials: sources of information* is an international annotated listing of sources of materials used to standardize analytical, physicochemical, and engineering methods.

Technical standards are a guide to recognized and proven methods, materials, and testing procedures in engineering of all kinds. The national authority in the United Kingdom is the British Standards Institution, incorporated in 1929 after evolving from the joint Engineering Standards Committee formed by a number of engineering institutions in 1901. It is recognized as the sole organization for promulgating national industrial standards and works through the medium of many committees and sub-committees consisting of representatives of appropriate, interested, bodies. The whole range of British Standards with short descriptive notes will be found in the *British Standards Yearbook* to which supplementary information is published in the monthly *BSI News*. Sectional lists are available, free of charge, from British Standards Institution, 2 Park Street, London, W1, of which SL 26, *Electrical Engineering*, is the most important, while others cover *Acoustics*, *Nomenclature*, *Abbreviations and Symbols*, etc. Typical British Standards are BS 3026: 1958: *Voltages for High-voltage d.c. Transmission Systems*, and BS 3549: 1963: *Methods for Measuring and Expressing the Performance of Television Receivers*.

International co-ordination is the object of the International Organization for Standardization which issues international recommendations rather than standards. Its 44 members are national committees, composed of representatives of the various technical and scientific organizations which deal with questions of standardization. Since 1947, ISO work in the electrical field has been carried out by the International Electrotechnical Commission (IEC) which is affiliated to ISO as its electrical division. A list of IEC Recommendations appears in the British Standards Institution Sectional List 26 mentioned above where there is also a list of publications of the International Commission on Rules for the Approval of Electrical Equipment (CEE). For further information on these international bodies see *International Scientific Organizations* by K. O. Murra (Library of Congress, 1962).

Other organizations than BSI in the United Kingdom issue regulations, standards, and codes of practice which are as important as the official British Standards. The Institution of Electrical Engineers, for example, issues *Regulations for the Electrical Equipment of Buildings* (1962).

In the more specialized field of broadcasting, the Radio Industry Council, a body co-ordinating the activities of the British Radio Equipment Manufacturers' Association (BREMA), the British Radio Valve Manufacturers' Association (BVA), the Electronic Engineering Association (EEA), and the Radio and Electronic Component Manufacturers' Federation (RECMF) is responsible for standardization and issues a series of specifications identified by the prefix *RIC*. Thus *RIC* 251 is for *Valveholders, Electronic, Receiver Types*.

The Radio Components Standardization Committee is a sub-committee of the Joint Electronics Standardization Committee of the Ministry of Defence. Specifications are issued as a basis for standardization of radio, telecommunications, and allied components (excluding valves) used in the various government activities. DEF-5000 is an important basic specification covering *General Requirements for Service Telecommunication Equipment*, while DEF-5001 relates to *General Specification for Electronic Components*. Earlier specifications had the prefix RC, thus RCS 352 *Specification for Waveguides, Couplings*.

More general specifications for government purposes are listed in the Ministry of Aviation's *Aircraft Material Specifications—DTD series* and in the Ministry of Defence's *Index of Defence Specifications* both published by HMSO.

In the United States, the national standards body is the American Standards Association which is more of a co-ordinating and less of an issuing body than the British Standards Institution. An annual *Catalog of American Standards* is published and special lists such as *The 400 American Standards in the Electrical Field*.

The American Society for Testing and Materials is of considerable importance and issues ASTM Standards in 7 volumes triennially with supplements in between (Fig. 10). The two organizations now merged to form the Institute of Electrical and Electronics Engineers, the Institute of Radio Engineers, and the American Institute of Electrical Engineers, have both been responsible for much work in the standards field. The IRE issued *Current Standardization Reports* using as a prefix the year of publication, as 55 IRE 2.S1, *Standards on Antennas and Waveguides: definitions for waveguide components*, 1955.

One of the largest standards published anywhere was produced

Scope

1. This specification covers round wire in three classes from 0.010 to 0.075 in. in diameter for use as grid siderods in electron tubes and in a form applicable to direct feeding into equipment employed in grid fabrication.

Description of Terms

2. (a) *Yield Strength.*—The stress developed at 1 per cent elongation of a 10-in. gage length.

(b) *Working Range.*—The difference between the yield strength and the ultimate strength.

(c) *Breaking Strength.*—The stress at which the specimen breaks.

(d) *Ultimate Strength.*—The maximum stress developed within a test specimen.

(e) *Elongation.*—The per cent of stretch of a 10-in. gage length.

[1] Under the standardization procedure of the Society, this specification is under the jurisdiction of the ASTM Committee F-1 on Materials for Electron Tubes and Semiconductor Devices.

[2] Accepted by the Administrative Committee on Standards, April 13, 1957.

Chemical Composition

3. The wire shall conform to the requirements as to chemical composition specified in Table I.

Mechanical Properties

4. The wire shall conform to the following requirements as to mechanical properties for the class of wire designated:

Class I.—Wire supplied as Class I shall bend between 30 and 60 deg when tested at the gram-centimeter torque value specified in Table II. The torque values apply to material ready for use on the grid-producing machine.

Class II.—Wire supplied as Class II shall conform to the requirements as to yield strength, with a tolerance of approximately ±15 per cent (as shown in pounds, min and max), working range, and elongation as specified in Table III.

Class III.—Wire supplied as Class III shall conform to the requirements as to yield strength, with a tolerance of approximately ±10 per cent (as shown

Fig. 10.   ASTM *Tentative Specification F9-59T*, 1959. (By permission of the American Society for Testing and Materials, Philadelphia.)

by the Institute of Radio Engineers Inc. in September 1962. This was *IRE Standards on Electron Tubes: methods of testing, 1962*, 160 pages long and too big to be published in the *Proceedings of the IRE* as is the usual practice. Of particular interest to electrical engineers, radio engineers, and physicists it contains complete information on the testing of all kinds of electron tubes including descriptions of test equipment and precautions to be observed to ensure validity of test results. Some idea of the enormous amount of work which is necessary in the preparation of standards generally may be obtained by quoting the figures relating to this standard.

The Standard was the result of 7 years' activity of the IRE Electron Tubes Committee during which 167 experienced research and engineering workers in the field of electron tubes devoted approximately 20,000 man-hours of careful deliberation. This does not include outside investigation and other time spent outside the Committee and altogether perhaps over 50,000 man-hours were devoted to this document.

In 10 parts, the Standard contains in its first 3 parts completely revised versions of *IRE Standards on Electron Tubes: methods of testing, 1950* and a minor revision of *IRE Standards on Methods of Measuring Noise in Linear Twoparts, 1959*. The remaining 6 parts contain totally new, previously unpublished methods of testing. References, bibliographies, and new definitions of terms are provided in many parts.

The AIEE's *Standards on Electrical Machinery and Apparatus* was published as a list in *Electrical Engineering*, June 1958, pp. 66A–67A. Another standards-issuing body in the United States is the Electronic Industries Association of which REC-138 *Recording Tapes* and TR-142 *Microwave Housing Facilities* are examples. The Society of Motion Picture and Television Engineers (SMPTE) issues numerous standards in its field which are first published in the *Journal of the SMPTE* and also supplies test films which are widely used in the United States by the television industry as yardsticks for setting performance objectives of new and operational equipment.

The National Association of Broadcasters (NAB) publishes standards particularly concerned with mechanical, magnetic, and optical recording and reproducing. See *NAB Engineering Handbook*, edited by A. Prose Walker (5th edn., 1960). The National Electrical Manufacturers' Association (NEMA) issues over 150 standards for apparatus and equipment.

Questions

1. Select any handbook from within the whole field of electrical engineering and discuss its value and limitations to various types of user.

2. Taking one important branch of electrical engineering and, using the pertinent handbooks, treatises, and selected textbooks, compile a bibliography of not more than 50 references.

3. Explain the importance of standards to electrical engineers.

4. Examine any standard relevant to testing materials or methods and write an abstract intended for a design engineer.

CHAPTER 5

Encyclopedias, Dictionaries and Translations
UDC 621.3(03)

THE difference between encyclopedias and dictionaries is mainly one of degree. The encyclopedia discusses, illustrates, and enlarges upon topics; the dictionary defines words, terms, and symbols. There is little noticeable difference between some shorter encyclopedias and some fuller dictionaries, while some works are called encyclopedic dictionaries. In addition, some publications contain a mixture of longer, encyclopedic-type entries and shorter dictionary-type definitions.

General encyclopedias are useful for the broad backgrounds to technical and scientific subjects and particularly for historical and biographical information. They are often some years in the press and, despite various procedures for keeping up to date, will probably not be satisfactory for the latest information and news of developments. The yearbooks published in conjunction with most general encyclopedias, however, will often help to solve this problem if the reader can remember to consult them along with the main work.

The better known encyclopedias include the *Encyclopaedia Britannica*, American-owned but with a London editorial staff responsible for about half of the contents; *Collier's Encyclopedia*, American, good for scientific subjects; *Encyclopedia Americana*; *Chambers's Encyclopaedia*, the standard British encyclopedia; and *The World Book Encyclopedia*, another American publication aimed particularly at young people and valuable for up-to-date

The great advances of the past in electrical engineering are closely associated with certain inventions and discoveries which have made practical uses of electricity and magnetism. Throughout the history of electrical engineering, there have been eras of accelerated engineering activity that are closely identified with important discoveries by a relatively few scientists and engineers. In considering the historical development and present scope of electrical engineering, it is convenient to consider five eras of development.

First era. As early as the latter part of the sixteenth century, experimenters were exploring the behavior of static electricity. W. Gilbert (1540–1603), personal physician to Queen Elizabeth I, experimented with electric charges and discharges. In 1750 Benjamin Franklin proved that lightning was electrical in nature. Neither investigator discovered anything that was significant from the standpoint of the applications of electricity. Discovery of the presence of magnetism in certain rocks preceded the earliest knowledge of electricity. Such knowledge was common about 600 B.C. Applications of electrical knowledge were completely absent in this era. *See* ELECTRICITY; MAGNETISM.

Electrons possess negative charge; hence the direction of current flow is opposite to that of the flow of electrons. In a solid, however, electrons may, under certain conditions, move under the influence of an electric field in such a manner that the net effect is the same as though positively charged carriers of approximately electronic mass were responsible for the current flow. It is then common to speak of current due to holes, these holes being thought of as charge carriers of positive mass and charge (*see* HOLES IN SOLIDS). Frequently, especially in the case of polyvalent metals (and also in semiconductors), the experimental results are described most conveniently by assuming that holes, as well as ordinary electrons, contribute to charge flow. In the theory of conductivity one then speaks of a two-band model.

In the more general sense the theory of electrical conductivity of metals encompasses all phenomena which relate to the transport of electrons in metals. This includes the thermoelectric effects (Peltier, Thomson, and Seebeck effects), the isothermal magnetic effects (Hall, Corbino, and magnetoresistance effects), and the thermomagnetic effects (Nernst, Ettinghausen, and Righi-Leduc effects). Moreover, since transport of charge is accompa-

FIG. 11. *Encyclopedia of Science and Technology*, Vol. 4. (Copyright McGraw-Hill Book Company, Inc. Used by permission.)

concise entries on all subjects. Smaller encyclopedias range from *Everyman's Encyclopaedia* to many 1- or 2-volume works.

Special encyclopedias include the very useful *McGraw-Hill Encyclopedia of Science and Technology* (Fig. 11), 15 volumes, 2nd edn., 1966 and kept up to date and supplemented by the *McGraw-Hill Yearbook of Science and Technology*. There are over 2000 contributors to this work (mostly American) whose aim is to give information to "any person of modest technical training who wants to obtain information outside his particular specialization". Its American bias must be borne in mind, but this condition applies of course (for non-American readers) to many otherwise very useful reference books.

Van Nostrand's Scientific Encyclopedia (Princeton, NJ, 3rd edn., 1958) is a comprehensive work in 1 volume containing about 15,000 entries, some of which are brief definitions, others of comparatively considerable length. *Chambers's Technical Dictionary*, edited by C. F. Tweney and L. E. C. Hughes, was published in 1958 (3rd edn.) and includes a supplement containing nearly 5000 definitions of new terms.

A new German work to be completed in 17 volumes is *Lueger Lexikon der Technik*, edited by H. Franke, of which the first 10 volumes appeared between 1960 and 1966, each dealing with a particular subject area, for example, vol. 2, Electrotechniques and Atomics.

Encyclopedias and dictionaries on physics and chemistry will also be of use to the electrical engineer. Fuller information on these will be found in the companion volumes of this series, *How to find out about Physics* and *How to find out in Chemistry*,

The Encyclopaedic Dictionary of Physics, edited by J. Thewlis (of the AERE, Harwell), is a modern comprehensive work published by Pergamon Press, 1961–64, in 9 volumes of which the eighth contains subject and author indexes. The ninth is a multilingual glossary (Fig. 12) in English, French, German, Spanish, Russian, and Japanese. Contributions to the whole work are from mainly British and American sources although there are contributors from other countries. Articles vary in

No.	English	French	German	Spanish	Russian	Japanese
3906	electron luminescence	7631	3013	8065	5243	1446
3907	electron magnetic moment	8374	7323	8881	5376	1576
3908	electron mass	7788	3014	8265	5486	1545
3909	electron microscope	8185	3015	8717	13209	1489
3910	electron-microscope condenser lens	7280	6266	7770	4476	1492
3911	electron-microscope resolving power	9974	830	10076	8954	1491
3912	electron microscopy	8207	3016	8710	13160	1490
3913	electron mirror	1519	3053	5256a	13181	1464
3914	electron momentum	6645	2992	8873	3584	1570
3915	electron multiplier	8508	3084	8995	13219	1409
3916	electron-neutron interaction	6824	13189	7360	13179	1568
3917	electron noise	1253	3027	11670	13042	1575
3918	electron optics	8953	3017	9419	13163	1497
3919	electron orbits	8982	2963	9449	6838	1494
3920	electron pair	9089	3018	9564	13190	1562

FIG. 12. Thewlis's *Encyclopaedic Dictionary of Physics*, Glossary. (Copyright Pergamon Press.)

length and, except for the very brief entries, are signed. Many carry bibliographies. A series of Annual Supplements to the *Dictionary* is planned to deal with new topics and new developments in topics previously covered. Survey articles are also to be included. The first supplement appeared in 1966.

A few encyclopedias and dictionaries are devoted specifically to electrical engineering. *Newnes Concise Encyclopaedia of Electrical Engineering*, edited by M. G. Say, was published in 1962 and has 130 contributors. *The Practical Dictionary of Electricity and Electronics* by R. L. Oldfield was published in Chicago by the American Technical Society in 1958 and defines about 4500 terms. It also includes a 24-page section of tables, diagrams, formulae, etc. Other British publications include the *Dictionary of Heavy Electrical Engineering* by G. W. Stubbings, Spon, 1948; a longer work *The New Electrical Encyclopaedia*, edited by S. G. B. Stubbs in 4 volumes (London, Waverley Book Co., *c.* 1953) and designed for "working engineers"; and S. R. Roget's *A Dictionary of Electrical Terms* (Pitman) which reached its 4th edition in 1941.

Published by the British Standards Institution is a *Glossary of Terms used in Electrical Engineering* (BS 205), 1943, with later amendments, consisting of 8 parts, including an index, which are available separately.

Language Dictionaries

In choosing a language dictionary for use, various points should be kept in mind. The currency of the dictionary is important, particularly in electronics and other branches of electrical engineering where rapid developments are taking place. Whether or not the dictionary has definitions as well as straightforward translations is important, and a work published by or on behalf of a learned society or similar body will carry particular authority. Naturally, the range of languages to be covered must be considered and it is also significant to determine whether it is English

Q-FACTOR

QUADRUPLE SYSTEM

No.	English GB and US	Subject		Français French	Español Spanish	Italiano Italian	Nederlands Dutch	Deutsch German	No.
1951	Q-factor	gen	A measure and rate of or materials.	facteur m de mérite, facteur m de qualité	factor m de calidad	fattore m di merito	kwaliteits-factor m	Gütefaktor m	1951
1952	Q-factor, magnification factor GB	gen	Quotient of als of an o the assumed	coefficient m de surtension	factor m de sobretensión	fattore m di sovratensione	overspannings-factor m	Überspannungs-faktor m	1952
1953	Q-meter	gen	Apparatus f	Q-mètre m	medidor m del factor de calidad, Q-metro m	misuratore m del fattore di merito, Q-metro m	q-meter m	Q-Messer m	1953
1954	quad	gen	An assembl	étoile f, quarte f	cuadrete m, cuádruple m	bicoppia f	ster f	Vierer m, Viererseil n	1954
1955	quad cable GB, spiral-four-quad US, star-quad cable GB	gen	A cable con	câble m à plusieurs quartes en étoile	cable m cuádruple de parejas	cavo m bicoppia	tweeparen-kabel m	Sternvierer-kabel n	1955

FIG. 13. *Dictionary of Amplification, Modulation.* (By permission of the Elsevier Publishing Co. Ltd.)

or American usage that has been taken as the English base for the dictionary.

The multilingual technical dictionaries published by Elsevier in Amsterdam deserve special mention. They cover a fairly closely defined field such as radar, antennas, and television (in 1 volume) although to preserve their encyclopedic nature some overlapping is inevitable. The basic list of words or phrases is in English (with American usage differentiated where relevant) and each is numbered and accorded a subject heading followed by a full definition (Fig. 13). Equivalent terms are then given in French, Spanish, Italian, Dutch, and German across the facing page. Each language has its index referring to the basic list. For some subjects there are supplementary volumes in Russian and Swedish. Among these dictionaries is *Elsevier's Electrotechnical Dictionary in Six Languages* (Fig. 14), edited by W. E. Clason, 1965, and *Elsevier's Dictionary of General Physics in Six Languages*, 1962.

Another polyglot work is the International Electrotechnical Commission's *International Electrotechnical Vocabulary* published by the Commission in Geneva in 22 groups, 2nd edn., 1954 onwards. French, English, German, Spanish, Italian, Dutch, Polish, and Swedish are the main languages covered, but there are also special supplements for Russian and Chinese.

For French, German, and English, H. Thali's *Technical Dictionary of the Terms used in Electrical Engineering*, 4th edn., Lucerne, Thali, 1960, in 3 volumes, is a standard work. *Dictionary of Electrical Engineering, German–English, English–German*, 1959, by H. F. Schwenkhagen, published in Essen by Girardet, has been well reviewed, while on a wider scale A. Webel's *German–English Technical and Scientific Dictionary*, 3rd edn., Routledge & Kegan Paul, 1963, has been specially prepared for the technical translator.

Guides to dictionaries include *A Guide to Foreign Language Grammars and Dictionaries*, edited by A. J. Walford (The Library Association, 1964); the *UNESCO Bibliography of Monolingual Scientific and Technical Glossaries* (2 vols., 1955–59); the *UNESCO Bibliography of Interlingual Scientific and Technical*

351   POWER FACTOR OF THE FUNDAMENTAL

4790 POWER COMPONENT OF THE CURRENT, ACTIVE COMPONENT OF THE CURRENT, ENERGY COMPONENT OF THE CURRENT, IN-PHASE COMPONENT OF THE CURRENT
f composante f active du courant
e componente f activa de la corriente
i componente f attiva della corrente
nl werkstroomcomponent m
d Wirkstromkomponente f

4791 POWER COMPONENT OF THE VOLT-AMPERES, ACTIVE COMPONENT OF THE VOLT-AMPERES, ENERGY COMPONENT OF THE VOLT-AMPERES, IN-PHASE COMPONENT OF THE VOLT-AMPERES

4795 POWER CUT-OFF RELAY
f relais m de coupure de courant
e relé m de corte de corriente
i relè m indicatore di mancanza di corrente
nl stroomonderbrekingsmeldrelais n
d Stromunterbrechungsmelderelais n

4796 POWER DIRECTION RELAY
f relais m directionnel de puissance
e relé m direccional de potencia
i relè m direzionale di potenza
nl vermogensrichtingsrelais n
d Leistungsrichtungsrelais n

4797 POWER FACTOR
f facteur m de puissance
e factor m de potencia
i fattore m di potenza
nl arbeidsfactor m
d Leistungsfaktor m

Fig. 14. *Electrotechnical Dictionary in Six Languages*, 1965. Compiled by W. E. Clason. (By permission of the Elsevier Publishing Co. Ltd.)

Dictionaries, 4th edn., 1961 (with supplement 1964); and the Library of Congress *Foreign Language–English Dictionaries: special subject dictionaries*, 1955.

Translations

It has been estimated that the engineer or scientist speaking only English is separated from at least one-third of the world's scientific and technical literature. With the development of technology in such countries as Russia, Japan, and China, this situation will get worse. Solutions to this problem include the learning of foreign languages; the use of comprehensive English-language abstracts, digests, and reviews as a substitute for the original material; cover-to-cover translations of important journals; the commissioning of translations of individual papers and reports as they are required, and the identification and location of single translations already made.

C. W. Hanson, in *The Foreign Language Barrier in Science and Technology* (Aslib, 1962), shows that it is possible for a scientist to acquire a reading knowledge of Russian after from about 50 to 200 hours of tuition. He urges the promotion of such courses and investigation of the effectiveness of similar courses in other languages.

Meanwhile, the use of English-language guides to world literature (see Chapter 6 on Abstracting Services) gives a key to information likely to be of use. Cover-to-cover translations of selected Russian and east European journals is undertaken in several countries particularly the United States and the United Kingdom.

The National Lending Library for Science and Technology sponsors the regular cover-to-cover translations of sixteen important Russian scientific periodicals. In addition it collects and loans almost 200 other cover-to-cover translations and abstracts journals which are produced elsewhere. This basic Russian collection is augmented by a growing collection of translations of individual articles from other Russian scientific publications and by translations of books. By the end of 1966 this collection contained over 60,000 translations of articles and over 1500 translations of books.

In addition, the National Lending Library will undertake translations for other organizations provided that the latter agree to edit the draft of the translations which may later be made available to other users.

A Commonwealth Index to Unpublished Scientific and Technical Translations is maintained by Aslib, 3 Belgrave Square, London, SW 1. It is a location index to mostly unpublished translations of articles from all languages into English made in the principal countries of the Commonwealth. It also includes translations collected since January 1959 by CFSTI and the Special Libraries Association (see below). These translations made for individual needs may be borrowed, bought or otherwise obtained from the organization possessing the original. By means of this, and similar, smaller indexes, unnecessary duplication can be avoided. In the electrical field, for example, the Information Services of the Central Electricity Generating Board maintains an index of all translations of relevance. They are also responsible for a series of translations which now totals more than 3800.

In the United States the Clearing House for Federal Scientific and Technical Information, the Special Libraries Association Translations Center (the John Crerar Library, Chicago), and the Library of Congress are particularly concerned with the collection and listing of translations. A useful guide to the subject, not completely confined to American facilities, is *Translators and Translations: Services and Sources*, edited by Frances E. Kaiser, New York, Special Libraries Association, 2nd edn., 1965. *Providing US Scientists with Soviet Scientific Information* by Boris I. Gorokhoff (National Science Foundation, 1962) is also valuable.

The US Department of Commerce Clearing House for Federal, Scientific, and Technical Information issues twice a month its *Technical Translations* which lists on an international basis translated scientific and technical reports, periodicals, and books

arranged in subject order. Most of the material has been translated into English, but some is in other west European languages.
Much of the material is of Soviet origin, but works from eastern
and western European countries are also cited as well as from
Japan and Communist China. Information given includes the
price and agency from which the translation can be obtained
although most of the literature is available from the Clearing
House, the (American) Special Libraries Association Translations Center, or the European Translations Centre in Delft,
The Netherlands.

The *NLL Translations Bulletin*, published monthly, carries in
each issue several English translations of important Russian
papers followed by lists of currently received translations held
in the National Lending Library's loan collection.

The National Research Council of Canada produces, through
the Translations Section of the National Science Library, a *List
of Technical Translations* (with supplements) of material in its
own series. The Council also maintains a Canadian Translations
Index.

In the atomic energy field a valuable contribution is made by
Transatom Bulletin, published monthly by Transatom, which was
set up in Brussels by Euratom to collect and disseminate information on translations. Transatom maintains a master card file
of all data relating to translations of interest, particularly in
unfamiliar languages.

Questions

1. Compare the treatment of two electrical engineering subjects in the
McGraw-Hill *Encyclopedia of Science and Technology* (and supplementary
volumes) with any 1-volume technical encyclopedia.

2. Enumerate the useful features of an encyclopedia, demonstrating by
examples.

3. Which language dictionaries are of particular importance in electrical
engineering libraries?

4. Examine any glossary or dictionary of terms in your field for currency
and relevance.

5. Take the current issue of any one important abstracting service and
compare the number of foreign-language citations with those from English
language sources.

CHAPTER 6

Periodicals, Abstracts and Indexes, Annual Reviews of Progress, Buyers' Guides and Directories UDC 621.3(05)

Periodicals

SINCE the publication of the first scientific journals in 1665, the *Journal des Scavans*, published in Paris, and the *Philosophical Transactions of the Royal Society* (London), periodicals have grown increasingly both in importance to the communication of scientific and technical knowledge and in numbers. Various estimates of the numbers of scientific and technical periodicals currently published throughout the world have been made. These estimates vary between 25,000 significant titles and 100,000 but the true figure is under 30,000.

The journal, or periodical, has been the means of disseminating information about ideas, research, and other work done as widely and as quickly as possible. Now, however, even the journal itself is under criticism, much of it justifiable, for failing to do these tasks as well as it should. Various alternatives to the scientific periodical have been suggested, including the publication of separate papers as pamphlets and the use of tape recordings or microtexts, but none have yet superseded the periodical nor show signs of doing so.

Periodicals may, for convenience, be classified into several categories. Of first importance are those reporting original work or critical reviews, and these are mostly published by the major learned societies such as the Institute of Electrical and Electronic Engineers, the Institution of Electrical Engineers, and the Institution of Electronic and Radio Engineers, or by governmental departments or agencies such as the Post Office. A second class is that of the technical periodicals issued by firms engaged in the electrical engineering industry such as Philips or GEC. Many of these firms also issue house journals which are of some value for news of personalities, new developments, etc., but the technical journals often contain results of research and other original contributions to knowledge. Another category altogether is that of the commercially published trade journals, such as *Electrical Times*, issued largely as advertising media but having of necessity for survival to carry good standard editorial matter.

The *Proceedings of the Institution of Electrical Engineers* is published monthly and its contents are divided into three categories—Electronics; Power; and Control and Science. Each issue contains some 30 or so papers, each with a synopsis and bibliography, and sometimes with an account of any discussion following the delivery of the paper. Not all papers have been presented to members before publication, however. Correspondence referring to published papers is also printed in the *Proceedings*. The three sections are also available separately as quarterly periodicals under their appropriate titles: *Electronics Record*, *Power Record*, and *Control and Science Record*. An index to the *Proceedings* which, in one form or another, have been published since 1872, is published for each 10-year period as well as an annual one. The *Proceedings*, in fact, started life in 1872 as the *Journal of the Society of Telegraph Engineers* until 1889 when it became the *Journal of the IEE* (until 1948).

The present journal of the Institution is published under the title of *Electronics and Power*, although from 1955 to 1963 it was known simply as the *Journal of the Institution of Electrical Engineers* (new series). *Electronics and Power*, which appears monthly, contains feature articles, special features, notes and news, correspondence, announcements to members, new products information, and usefully evaluative book reviews. It also carries a considerable amount of advertising in contrast to the *Proceedings* which contains a few advertisements only. There is an annual index.

The Institute of Electrical and Electronics Engineers (formed in 1963 by an amalgamation of the Institute of Radio Engineers and the American Institute of Electrical Engineers) has published since 1963 its *Proceedings of the IEEE* which continues the volume numbering of its predecessor, the *Institute of Radio Engineers Proceedings*. It contains some longer papers written at the most advanced level—many shorter items submitted as correspondence, book reviews, notices, news, and advertisements. Frequently issues are devoted to a single subject and form an important contribution to the literature of that subject.

The journal of the IEEE is *IEEE Spectrum*, a monthly publication considered to be the "core publication" of the Institute to assist its membership in keeping informed about new developments. It contains a number of well-illustrated feature articles at a level to be understood by the majority of members as well as news, reports and notices of meetings, book reviews, abstracts, and so on.

The IEEE also publishes the *IEEE Student Journal* and *Transactions* for each of the 31 groups with specialized interests in the electrical and electronics field. Details of some of these will be found in the appropriate chapters which follow.

Two weekly British periodicals to keep the electrical engineer up to date are *Electrical Review* (an Iliffe publication) and *Electrical Times*. Both contain general articles, news and notes, business information, and many advertisements. Playing a similar role in the United States is McGraw-Hill's *Electrical World* in a more attractive format than either.

Devoted almost entirely to advertisements and descriptions of new equipment is *Electrical Equipment*, one of a series of similar controlled circulation periodicals. An occasional article is useful as a very general introduction to some such topic as sheathing materials for electric cables.

Other general electrical engineering journals of importance at research level include the *Post Office Electrical Engineers' Journal* (quarterly), which deals with all aspects of Post Office electrical engineering, and the *Institute of Electrical Engineers of Japan Journal* which is in Japanese but has title and contents page in English.

East European Periodicals

Naturally, the periodicals published in the Communist countries of eastern Europe are issued by governments or governmental agencies. Top priority has been given in these countries to the development of the national scientific and technical effort, and many important research institutes have been established. *Archiwum Elektrotechniki* (Archives of Electrical Engineering) is a quarterly containing research papers in Polish issued by the Institute of Basic Technical Problems, Polish Academy of Sciences, but it also contains summaries in English, French, and Russian.

From Yugoslavia comes *Elektrotehniski Vestnik* (Electrotechnical Review), a monthly co-operative effort by several institutions and factories in that country and which covers electrical engineering generally. It has summaries in English, French, and German.

A Hungarian technical journal of electrical engineering and applied physics is published quarterly by the Polytechnical University in Budapest. This is *Periodica Polytechnica, Electrical Engineering*, and the articles are in either English or German.

The important Soviet journal *Elektrotekhnika* is now available in full English translation under the title *Soviet Electrical Engineering* (Faraday Press, New York, 1965–).

Manufacturing firms

Among the technical journals published by manufacturing firms in the United Kingdom are:

AEI Engineering (bi-monthly).

The English Electric Journal (bi-monthly), published since 1920.

GEC Journal (quarterly).

These publish articles about their own new products and processes at a technical but not highly specialized level.

Some lavishly produced European technical house journals are available in English. The quarterly *AEG Progress* of the Allgemeine Elektricitäts-Gesellschaft, Berlin-Grunewald is one example and *The Brown Boveri Review* (Switzerland) another.

From the gigantic Philips firm in the Netherlands comes *Philips Technical Review* (monthly), available in English, Dutch, French, and German editions, and the more magazine-type *Philips Forum* is published from the English branch.

ACEC Review, from the Belgian Ateliers de Constructions Electriques de Charleroi, is also published in the four languages mentioned above.

A number of Japanese manufacturing firms produce English language editions of their house publications:

Mitsubishi Denki Engineer (irregular).
Toshiba Review (quarterly).
Hitachi Review (monthly).

The last-named is at research level rather more than the other two, and also more specialized are *Mitsubishi Denki Laboratory Reports* (quarterly, in English) and the Matsushita Electric Industrial Company's *National Technical Report* which is in Japanese but contains fairly full abstracts in English. *NEC Research and Development* (twice a year) is entirely in English.

Using Periodicals

The first steps towards using periodicals include finding out what exists in a given subject field and whether such titles are at a relevant level. There is no complete international guide to periodicals, but *Ulrich's International Periodicals Directory* (Fig. 15), now in its 11th edition (1965, vol. 1), contains about one-half of the world's current output of scientific and technical journals estimated to be some 26,000. Details of frequency of publication, publisher's address, subscription price, and notes on the main features are given together with names of abstracting and indexing

F

Engineering, Electrical (cont.)

COOPERATIVE ELECTRICAL RESEARCH. 1956. q. 3s.6d.per no. Ed. N.G. Deed. Electrical Research Association, Cleve Rd., Leatherhead, Surrey, Eng. charts. illus. cum.index every 2 years. circ. 2000. Indexed: Rub.Abstr. Sci.Abstr.

CURRENT PAPERS FOR THE PROFESSIONAL ELECTRICAL AND ELECTRONICS ENGINEER. 1964. m. 20s.($3.) Ed. L.M. Wallace. Institution of Electrical Engineers, Savoy Place, London W.C.2, Eng. bibl.(To be abstracted later in Sci.Abstr.)

ELECTRIC TECHNOLOGY U.S.S.R. (English translation of "Elektrichestvo") 1957. q. $100.(660s.) Pergamon Press, Oxford, Eng., and 122 E. 55th St., New York, N.Y. 10022. charts. Indexed: Chem.Abstr.

ELECTRICAL COMMUNICATION LABORATORY. REVIEW. Vol.12,1964. bi-m. Yen 1200. Ed. Tsunetaka UEDA. Electrical Communication Laboratory, Nippon Telegraph and Telephone Public Corp., 535, 3-tyome, Midori-tyo, Musasino-si, Tokyo, Japan. bibl. charts. illus. Indexed: Chem.Abstr. Eng.Ind. Sci.Abstr.

ELECTRICAL CONTRACTOR AND RETAILER. See ELECTRICITY

ELECTRICAL ENGINEERING. 1887. m. $12. Ed. Charles S. Rich. American Institute of Electrical Engineers, 345 E. 47th St., New York 17, N.Y. abstr. adv. bibl. bk.rev. illus. tr.lit. index. circ. 67,000. Indexed: A.S.& T.Ind. Chem.Abstr. Eng.Ind. Fuel Abstr. Met.Abstr. Sci.Abstr.

ELECTROTEHNICA. (Text in Rumanian; summaries in English, French, German and Russian) 1952. m. 30 lei for individuals; 100 lei for institutions. Ed. Dr. Aurel Avramescu. Ministerului Industriei Constructiilor de Masini, str. Ion Ghica Nr.3, Bucharest, Rumania. adv. bk.rev. charts. illus. pat. tr.mk. index. circ. 2400. Indexed: Chem.Abstr. Sci.Abstr.

ELEKTROTEHNIČAR. See ELECTRICITY

ELEKTROTEHNIKA. Electrical Engineering. 1950. m. 6000 din.($8.) Ed. Franjo Hidvegi. Jugoslovenski Centar za Tehničku i Naučnu Dokumentaciju, ul. Adm. Geprata br.16, Belgrade, Yugoslavia. abstr. bk.rev. pat.

ELEKTROTEHNIŠKI VESTNIK. See ELECTRONICS.

ELEKTROTEKHNIKA. (Formerly: Vestnik Elektropromysheln-nosti) (Komitet Elektrotekhnika, Komitet Coordinatsia Nay-xhnaissledovatelskich Rabot) 1928. m. 8 rub.40 kop.($11.) Ed. A.G. Iosifian. Khoromnyi, Tupik 4, Moscow 5-78, USSR. adv. bk.rev. charts. illus. circ. 6500. Indexed: Chem.Abstr. Sci.Abstr.

ELEKTROTEKNIKEREN. See ELECTRICITY

ELEKTROTEKNISK TIDSSKRIFT. See ELECTRICITY

ELTEKNIK; tidskrift for elektrisk kraftteknik, teleteknik och elektronik. (Text in English and Swedish) 1958. m.(Sept-June) Kr.30.($6.) Ed. Rolf Gezelius. Svenska Elektroingenjörers Riksförening, Sippvägen 28, Viggbyholm, Sweden. adv. bk.rev. charts. illus. tr.lit. index. circ. 4500. Indexed: Eng.Ind. Sci.Abstr.

FIG. 15. Ulrich's *International Periodicals Directory*, 11th edn. (By permission of R. R. Bowker Co., New York.)

services which refer to this particular periodical. *Guide to Current British Periodicals*, edited by Mary Toase (Library Association, 1962), gives rather fuller information for those published in the United Kingdom, while other directories such as *Willings' Press Guide* (annually) are useful. There are national guides to the publications of many individual countries. If the location of an existing set of a periodical is required the *British Union Catalogue of Periodicals* (BUCOP), now compiled in the National Central Library, together with its monthly supplements, should be used. The *World List of Scientific Periodicals* which for many years has been the standard location list in the United Kingdom (and whose abbreviations are used in many contexts) is now amalgamated with BUCOP. Many of the local co-operative schemes for industry and commerce publish their own finding lists, and the National Lending Library for Science and Technology, the Patent Office Library, and the Science Library all issued lists of current serials in their stocks in 1965. For the USA and Canada the essential union list is *The Union List of Serials* (New York, H. W. Wilson) supplemented by *New Serial Titles* (monthly with annual and 5-year Cumulations, Library of Congress).

Abstracts and Indexes

Throughout the world, in many languages, there are currently published about 26,000 scientific and technical journals. Some estimates have been much higher but this figure, according to the National Lending Library for Science and Technology, is likely to be the more realistic one. Hundreds of these journals deal directly with electrical engineering and its branches; many more deal with other subjects of importance to the electrical engineer and yet many others contain occasional articles useful as background information. It has long been impossible for the engineer or scientist to read more than a fraction of the periodical papers of interest to him, and the use of abstracts and indexes is an attempt to meet this problem.

Abstracts, or summaries, of papers, books, patents, reports, or any other similar documents, may range in length from several hundred words containing the substance of the original ("informative abstracts") to a brief description of a few words only ("indicative abstracts"). There is no hard and fast ruling on when an abstract ceases to be the one kind and becomes the other, but the terms are convenient for quick descriptions. Usually, although there are some exceptions, abstracts are non-critical and merely factually describe the contents of the original material. They may be written by the author, or based on author-abstracts, but more often are likely to be written by an abstractor, full-time or part-time, paid or unpaid.

Essential features of an abstract include full bibliographical details: author of original, title, name of journal (or publisher if a book or monograph), volume and part number, page numbers, and date of publication. Then follows the summary of the original textual material together with, sometimes, other useful information such as the status or employment of the author, and whether there are illustrations, bibliographical references, and other useful aids.

Abstracts may be published as complete services or they may appear as parts of journals. The text of both kinds of abstracts is usually in one language although a good service will, of course, take its original material from all relevant languages. The providers, or publishers, of abstracts may be governments, research associations or institutions, universities or other academic bodies or learned institutions or commercial organizations. In totalitarian countries like Russia, in which all bibliographical activities are state controlled, abstracting services are co-ordinated and centralized, but in other countries, except France, there is much overlapping of services, on the one hand, and gaps in provision on the other.

Indexes (not in this context indexes to individual periodicals or books) broadly consist of only the bibliographical details part of an abstract with entries arranged systematically. To this extent they are that much less useful than abstracts but they are cheaper and quicker to compile and publish and therefore have a useful part to play, particularly pending the appearance of abstracts of the material.

Specialized abstracts and indexes will be described in the appropriate subject chapters which follow, but an account of those covering the whole field, or most of it, follows here.

General Scientific and Technical Abstracts and Indexes

Of general services in English, the *Engineering Index* (which in fact is an abstracting service) is the longest established and has been published since 1885 (Fig. 16). It was available only in annual volumes from that date until 1928 when a weekly card service in 249 subject divisions was instituted. In 1962 the service became available in monthly parts and in January 1965 a start was made on a new project to publish it in monthly bulletins corresponding to individual disciplines. A pilot study was initiated in the electrical–electronics field in which articles are abstracted and then "deep-indexed" using the Engineering Joint Council–Battelle system of abstracting and indexing which is the basis for a co-ordinate index stored on tape. From terms selected for the deep index, subject headings are chosen for the published bulletin. It is intended that this method should provide many more analytical references to the material abstracted which includes periodicals, books, congresses, published reports, and some translations but not patents, or theses. Over 34,000 abstracts a year are published in the complete service from world literature in many languages.

The *British Technology Index* (Fig. 17), published monthly by the Library Association with annual cumulated volumes, is deliberately confined to references to current British periodicals of which just over 400 are indexed under specific subject headings arranged alphabetically. The *Applied Science and Technology Index* (Fig. 18) is published monthly (except August) by the H. W. Wilson Co., New York, with quarterly and annual cumulations. It succeeds the *Industrial Arts Index* which appeared from 1913 to 1957, covers about 200 English-language journals,

70

THE ENGINEERING INDEX – MARCH 1966

ELECTRIC MOTORS

Induction. See also Electric Motors—Control.

Equivalent Circuit for Single-Phase Motor Having Space Harmonics in Its Magnetic Field, L.W.BUCHANAN. IEEE—Trans on Power Apparatus & Systems v PAS-84 n 11 Nov 1965 p 999-1007. Equivalent circuit used for most single-phase motors with two windings is expanded to include motors having higher harmonics in magnetic field, produced by concentric stator windings concentrated into stator slots; mutual fields are described in equation form; their occurrence in single-phase induction motor is explained by graphical interpretation. Paper 31 TP 65-185.

Opredelenie kharakteristik nadezhnosti asinkhronnykh dvigatelei tipa ARP po dannym ekspluatatsii, A.S.LENOVICH. Izvestiya Vysshikh Uchebnykh Zavedenii, Elektromekhanika n 2 1965 p 140-5. Determination of characteristics of reliability of ARP induction motors from operational experience; reliability analysis of rolling mill motors.

Test Analysis for Equivalent Circuit Parameters of Precision Induction Motors, P.H.TRICKEY. IEEE—Trans on Power Apparatus & Systems v PAS-84 n 11 Nov 1965 p 1094-1103. Equivalent circuit of induction motor is modified by placing iron loss resistance branch between primary resistance and reactance, instead of in parallel with magnetizing reactance; using this circuit, open circuit and stalled rotor tests are analyzed for circuit parameters; curves are shown for obtaining secondary resistance when ratio of secondary to primary reactance is neither zero nor unity.

Protection. See also Industrial Plants—Power Supply.

Selecting Right Breaker for Motor Circuit, W.D.PATTON. Plant Eng v 19 n 9 Sept 1965 p 120-2. Molded-case circuit breakers, of both time-delay and instantaneous trip types, lend themselves well to use in motor circuits serving as short-circuit protection and as motor-disconnecting means; time-delay circuit breakers provide backup protection for overload relays or other overcurrent protection.

zione di energia reattiva, C.GIORDANA, E.ZAPPAROLI. Elettrotecnica v 51 n 9 Sept 1964 p 696-701. Control of reactive energy with undershoot commutation auto-transformer; Marinetto power plant in Turin, Italy, controls with exclusively static means, power factor of distribution network; gradual and continuous control of power factor is obtained by means of auto-transformer with undershoot commutation; equipment is described.

ELECTRIC POWER TRANSMISSION. See Electric Transmission.

ELECTRIC PRECIPITATORS. See Dust Collectors.

ELECTRIC PROPULSION. See Rocket Engines—Electric Propulsion.

ELECTRIC RAILROADS

Power Supply

Getting Power to London Midland Trains. Engineering v 200 n 5196 Nov 19 1965 p 643-5. Overhead equipment of newly electrified London Midland Region main line of British Railways can accommodate train speeds up to 100 mph and incorporates new ideas in insulation techniques; compound catenary equipment is used; insulator consists of glass fiber rod, 5 ft long, which is protected by ceramic bead sleeve; diagrams show arrangement of overhead structures.

Telephone Interference

Interference Problems in Vicinity of Electrified Railways, R. BUCKEL. Int Ry Congress Assn—Monthly Bul v 42 n 7 July 1965 p 490-508. Development and scope of technical discipline dealing with electric interference phenomena in railroad traction is reviewed, and effects on installations exposed to such interference are discussed; distinction is made between dangerous effects and disturbing effects; problems in connection with d-c and a-c operation; calculation of noise interference in telephone circuits caused by harmonics from rectifier locomotives can be approximate; preference is made to carry out statistical surveys on lines

FIG. 16. *Engineering Index*, March 1966. (By permission of Engineering Index Inc., New York.)

mostly American (hence the need for a British index), and its entries are also arranged alphabetically.

Electrical Engineering Abstracts and Indexes

The most important abstracting service for the electrical engineer is *Science Abstracts* produced by the Institution of Electrical Engineers with the co-operation of the Institute of Physics and the Physical Society, and the American Institute of Physics. It consists of two sections: Section A, *Physics Abstracts*, and Section B, *Electrical Engineering Abstracts*, and has appeared since 1898. From 1 January 1966 Section B has been renamed *Electrical and Electronic Abstracts* (Fig. 19) and a new section, *Control Abstracts*, started in June 1966 to coincide with the 3rd IFAC Congress. The three sections of Science Abstracts are issued monthly with the abstracts arranged by subject classification and with a monthly author index and semi-annual author and subject indexes. Five-year author and subject indexes have appeared for 1960–4, *Physics Abstracts* contain about 15,000 abstracts a year and *Electrical Engineering Abstracts* about 6000 abstracts from world sources.

The IEE also publishes monthly *Current Papers* (started in 1964), each issue of which contains at least 1200 titles of interest to electrical and electronics engineers, with bibliographic references taken from journals received in the Science Abstracts Office. (Delay period between receipt and notification varies between 2–4 weeks.) More than 900 journals are scanned in this way and items are listed under broad headings and then arranged by order of journal title (Fig. 20). A companion publication, *Current Papers in Physics*, started late 1965. A further publication, *Current Papers in Control*, appeared in June 1966.

ERA Weekly Abstracts—published by the British Electrical and Allied Industries Research Association—cover world literature, and are available on subscription to non-members of the Association. Coverage is electrical engineering, physics, and mathematics, and some 1500 abstracts a year are published. *Electrics Current* is a review of articles in periodicals held in the

ELECTRIC MOTORS, D.C., Permanent magnet
Equalising the performances of small permanent magnet
D.C. motors. J. Catherall. Mullard Technical Communica-
tions, 8 (Nov 65) p.236-8. il.

ELECTRIC MOTORS, Induction, Pole amplitude modulation
More scope for p.a.m. motors: summary of "Two-speed
induction motors using fractional-slot windings" by
G. H. Rawcliffe & W. Fong and "Wide-ratio two-speed
single-winding induction motors" by W. Fong. Electrical
Times, 148 (16 Dec 65) p.923-4

**ELECTRIC MOTORS, Induction, Rotors, Aluminium, Power
loss**
Origins of load losses in induction motors with cast aluminium rotors. N. Christofides. Proc. of Instn. of Electrical
Engrs., 112 (Dec 65) p.2317-32. il. refs.

ELECTRIC MOTORS, Induction, Starters
AQIP automatic starters [Vapormatic and the Statormatic]
Engineering, 200 (26 Nov 65) p.685-6. il.

ELECTRIC MOTORS, Induction, Ventilation. See VENTILA-
TION, Electric motors, Induction

ELECTRIC MOTORS, Power stations
Power-station auxiliaries—a review of some practical
aspects. J. R. Hazel. Electronics & Power, 11 (Dec
65) p.430-6. il.

ELECTRIC POWER SYSTEMS
Power in the region. J. C. Judson. Electrical Rev., 177 (10
Dec 65) p.866-7. il.

ELECTRIC POWER SYSTEMS
Related Headings:

ELECTRICAL DISCHARGE
Related Headings:
ARCS
GAS DISCHARGE
ELECTRICAL ENGINEERING
Related Headings:
A.C.
CAPACITANCE
CIRCUITS, Electric
COMMUNICATIONS, Engineering
CURRENT
D.C.
ELECTROMAGNETIC WAVES
ELECTRONICS
IMPEDANCE
NETWORKS, Electrical
POWER FACTOR
POWER PLANT
POWER SUPPLIES
RESISTIVITY
SWITCHING
THERMOELECTRICITY
VOLTAGE
ELECTRICAL ENGINEERING, Components
Related Headings:
BATTERIES
CAPACITORS
CONDUCTORS, Electrical
CONVERTERS

FIG. 17.   *British Technology Index* (monthly). (By permission of the Library Association.)

Commercial and Technical Reference Library at Acton, headquarters of the West London co-operative library system CICRIS. It appears monthly and is intended as a quick guide pending the appearance of *Electrical Engineering Abstracts* and similar comprehensive journals.

Much of the contents of *Chemical Abstracts*, which is divided into 74 sections, may be of value to electrical engineering particularly Sections 9, Electric and Magnetic Phenomena, and 15, Electrochemistry, as well as those dealing with ferrous and non-ferrous metals and alloys, rubber and plastics and ceramics.

Abstracting services in other languages than English, however comprehensive they are, are limited in use to those fluent in the language. However, mention should be made of *Referativnyi Zhurnal*, the great Russian abstracting service which appears as 16 abstract journals including *Elektrotekhnika i Energetika* which covers electrical engineering and power engineering and includes 55,000 abstracts a year from world literature — in Russian. Information is available in English on Russian material in *USSR Scientific Abstracts, Electronics and Electrical Engineering* and on other Communist countries in *East European Scientific Abstracts, Electronics and Electrical Engineering*, both published by the US Department of Commerce.

The Yugoslav Centre for Technical and Scientific Documentation issues a monthly Bulletin of Documentation in various sections of which *Bilten Dokumentacije: Elektrotehnika* (Bulletin of Documentation: Electrical Engineering) is relevant. It contains abstracts on physics and electrical engineering (including electronics) from Yugoslav and foreign periodicals, patents and standards.

A general technical Rumanian abstracts journal is *Documentare Tehnica* (Technical Documentation), monthly, in which the titles are in the language of the original but the abstracts are in Rumanian. On the other hand, *Hungarian Technical Abstracts* is a quarterly service, abstracting Hungarian periodicals published in Budapest, in English, German, and Russian, and *Polish Technical Abstracts*, also quarterly, contains, in English and Russian, reviews and abstracts of Polish literature.

MARCH 1966 113

ELECTRIC industries
Some challenges in power. W. L. Chadwick. il Civil Eng 35:82-4 N '65
See also
Electric contractors
Electric heating
Electric plants (central stations)
Electric utilities
National electrical manufacturers association
Radio apparatus industry

Materials

See also
Insulating materials

Great Britain

Electrical industry; presidential address. L. Drucquer. il Inst E E Proc 113:1-8 Ja '66

ELECTRIC instruments
Direct ratio readings from a Universal ratio set. diags Instruments & Control Systems 39:73-4 Ja '66
Eico 965 farad-ohm bridge analyzer. L. G. Sands. il diag Radio-Electronics 37:68-9 F '66
Field effect transistor converts transducer for use in a-c bridge. A. R. Greenfield and W. H. McCloskey. diag Electronics 39:84-5 F 7 '66
Low frequency bridge detector. C. D. Ferris and J. Bartholomew. diag R Sci Instr 36:1652-4 N '65
Resistivity bridge. il Wireless World 71:574 N '65
Simple tests speed motor troubleshooting with portable indicating instrument. R. Feldman. il diag Elec Constr & Maint 64:98-9+ D '65
Travelling-field theory of induction-type instruments and motors. H. E. M. Barlow. bibliog diags Inst E E Proc 112:1208-14 Je

Flashing

Generation and detection of subnanosecond light pulses; application to luminescence studies. J. Yguerabide. diags R Sci Instr 36:1734-42 D '65
High dc power, solid state switch for pulsing an arc lamp. T. A. Alexander and others. diag R Sci Instr 36:1707-9 D '65
Multiple watt submicrosecond high repetition rate light source and its application. R. C. Mackey and others. il diags R Sci Instr 36:1715-18 D '65
Safety lighting for winter equipment. H. R. Malott. il Pub Works 96:80-1 D '65

ELECTRIC lamps, Arc
Why glow-lamps glow. T. Jaski. il diags Radio-Electronics 37:53-5 F '66
See also
Electric lamps, Fluorescent
Electric lamps, Mercury vapor
Electric lamps, Xenon

ELECTRIC lamps, Fluorescent
Standardizing fluorescent lamp colors. diag Glass Ind 57:19+ Ja '66

Control

Performance characteristics of fluorescent lamps utilizing amalgam control of mercury -vapor pressure. G. S. Evans and P. E. Snyder. bibliog il Illum Eng 61:51-7 Ja '66

ELECTRIC lamps. Incandescent
New light sources and associated optical systems for theatre and television. T. M. Lemons and R. E. Levin. il diags Illum Eng 60:637-49 N '65
Quartz-iodine infrared heat lamp. L. T. Heinlein and W. R. Stephens. il Illum Eng 61:47-50 Ja '66

ELECTRIC lamps, Mercury vapor
Beam efficiency vs utilization. V. Bishop and others. il diags Illum Eng 60:626-34 N '65

FIG. 18. *Applied Science and Technology Index.* (By permission of the H. W. Wilson Co., New York.)

From Prague, *Prehled Technicke a Hospodarske Literatury; Energetika a Elektotechnika* (Review of Technical and Economic Literature; Electric Power and Electrical Engineering) abstracts, monthly, in Czechoslovakian, both domestic and foreign publications.

The Centre de Documentation du Centre National de la Recherche Scientifique (CNRS), Paris, publishes a comprehensive abstracting service in 24 parts known as *Bulletin Signalétique.* Section 9 is concerned with engineering, including electrical engineering, while Section 3 deals with physics, mechanics, acoustics, optics and thermodynamics and Section 4 with instrumentation, electronics, telecommunications, plasma physics, and electromagnetism and electricity generally.

In Germany, *Technisches Zentralblatt*, is an abstracting service in several parts of which *Abteilung Elektrotechnik*, published monthly, deals with electrical engineering and is particularly strong in references to patents.

Several countries publish abstracts in English of journals published in their own land as a means of publicizing their scientific and technical effort. One example is *Japan Science Review: mechanical and electrical engineering*, published quarterly since 1954 and containing abstracts and bibliographic references in English from Japanese literature providing also the Japanese titles and arranged by the UDC.

The Institute of Scientific and Technical Information of China, Peking, produces *Science Abstracts of China: technical sciences* bi-monthly. This covers engineering generally and is confined to abstracts in English from Chinese literature. An American produced *Communist Chinese Scientific Abstracts*, with a part entitled *Electronics and Electrical Engineering*, started publication in 1965 (Joint Publications Research Service, Washington, D.C.).

Finally, mention should be made of three internal literature services which may be seen in libraries although circulation is restricted somewhat: *AEI Research Laboratory Technical News Bulletin* (weekly, 2500 abstracts a year), *Central Electricity Generating Board Digest* (2000 abstracts a year), and the *Post Office*

MEASUREMENTS AND INSTRUMENTATION

621.317:681.142
PROPOSED AMERICAN STANDARD: CHARACTER SET FOR OPTICAL CHARACTER RECOGNITION.   See Abstr.18135

621.317.2
18514   HYDROSTATIC SPHERICAL BEARINGS.
O.I.Bogdanov and V.G.Danil'tsev.
Elektrotekhnika (USSR), 1965, No. 8, 18-24 (Aug.). In Russian.

Spherical bearings are one way of providing a sliding support. In a spherical bearing, a ball is supported by hydrostatic pressure in a cup. Three types of bearing are considered here: the diffuser-gap, where the radial gap between ball and cup increases from the centre outwards; the constant-gap type and the confuser-gap, where cup and ball are the same diameter, so that the gap decreases with distance from the centre. Each type can be built with either central or annular oil feed. A method of designing these types of hydrostatic spherical bearing is given. The type having a confuser gap has the best characteristics, and moreover it is easier to manufacture.
J.H.B. Gould

621.317.2
18515   NEW NORMA CROSSED COIL LINE RECORDERS. .
P. Pfeiffenstein.

621.317.331
18519   THE EFFECT OF PRESSURE AND TEMPERATURE ON THE ELECTRICAL RESISTANCE OF RUBIDIUM AND CAESIUM.   J.S.Dugdale and D.Phillips.
Proc.Roy. Soc. A (GB), Vol.287, No.1410, 381-402 (1965).

Measurements have been made of the electrical resistivity of rubidium and caesium at temperatures between 1.5 and $300°K$ and at pressures up to 3000 atm. From the results the authors have calculated the ideal resistivity and its pressure derivative both at constant pressure and at constant density. The results are compared with those of the lighter alkali metals and with theoretical predictions.

621.317.331:621.315.52
ELECTRICAL RESISTANCE OF IRON FILMS DEPOSITED AT LIQUID NITROGEN TEMPERATURE.   See Abstr.13958

621.317.38:621.316.172
DOES IT PAY TO MEASURE THE ELECTRICITY CONSUMPTION OF EACH FLAT IN AN APARTMENT HOUSE SEPARATELY.   See Abstr.18431-18432

621.317.61:621.313.3
18520   MEASUREMENT OF DYNAMIC MOMENT OF A.C.

Fig. 19.   *Electrical and Electronics Abstracts* (monthly).   (By permission of the Institution of Electrical Engineers.)

Engineering Department Research Branch Library Circular (fortnightly, lists of articles under journal title).

Guides to abstracting and indexing services include *A Guide to the World's Abstracting and Indexing Services in Science and Technology* (Washington, National Federation of Science Abstracting and Indexing Services, 1963); *Technological Abstracts originating in the British Commonwealth* (London, Department of Scientific and Industrial Research, 1963); *Bibliography of Engineering Abstracting Services*, ed. by M. M. Landuyt (New York, Special Libraries Association, 1955); "The coverage of heavy electrical engineering periodical literature by abstracts journals" by P. Clague (in *Journal of Documentation*, vol. 20, June 1964, pp. 70–75); and "Abstracting journals in the electronics field" by C. K. Moore (in *ASLIB Proc.*, vol. 13, March 1961, pp. 65–75).

Annual Reviews of Progress

A comparatively recent, and most important, innovation in publishing is the appearance of annual reviews of progress in many fields of science and technology. In some cases these consist of the proceedings of conferences and in others of specially written review articles. Most of them give extensive lists of literature references. A few publishers are prominent in this matter and under each are listed below some of the more useful reviews for the electrical engineer.

ACADEMIC PRESS, NEW YORK

   Advances in Computers (1960–)
   Advances in Control Systems (1964–)
   Progress in Control Engineering (1962–)
   Advances in Communication Systems (1965–)
   Advances in Electronics and Electron Physics (1948–)
      (Volume 20 (1964) contains a cumulative author index to
         volumes 1–20)
   Advances in Radio Research (1964–)
   Progress in Dielectrics (1959–)

CURRENT PAPERS April 1966

A METHOD OF SYSTEM IDENTIFICATION WITH RANDOM INPUTS.* J.S.Thorp et al. p.290

Proc.Instn Elect.Engrs Mar 66
SIMULATION OF A LOW-PASS TRANSMISSION SYSTEM FOR SAMPLED DATA.* A.J.Gibbs.p.443

Scientia Sinica Jan 66
ON THE ABSOLUTE STABILITY AND DEGREE OF ABSOLUTE STABILITY OF NONLINEAR CONTROL SYSTEMS. Kao Wei-bin.pp.107-22

Trans'Soc.Instrum.Technol.Mar 66
ANALYSIS AND SYNTHESIS OF A SEQUENTIAL DIGITAL SERVOMECHANISM. R.B.Solanki et al.pp.26-44
A METHOD FOR SYNTHESIZING THE HARMONIC RESPONSE OF A CONTROL SYSTEM INCORPORATING A NONLINEAR ELEMENT. J.Parnaby.pp.45-9

POWER

Generation

Advanced Energy Conversion Jan-Mar 66
THERMOMOLECULAR ENERGY CONVERTORS-I.ENGINE CYCLES. G.A.McLennan et al.pp.1-9
THERMOMOLECULAR ENERGY CONVERTORS-II.HEAT PUMPS AND ZERO-WORK REFRIGERATORS. G.A.McLennan et al. pp.11-24

Apparatus and devices

GEC.J.Sci.Technol No 1,66
ELECTROSTATIC CLUTCHES BASED ON THE JOHNSEN-RAHBEK EFFECT. R.W.Dudding et al.pp.2-8

Siemens Rev.Feb 66
HIGH-CAPACITY BRAKING RESISTORS FOR ELECTRIC LOCOMOTIVES E10 AND E03. Czerny et al.pp.54-8

Transformation

Elect.Times 17 Feb 66
MONITORING DRYNESS IN POWER TRANSFORMERS, PART 1. B.Berger et al. pp.239-42

Elect.Times 3 Mar 66
AUTOMATIC INSULATION DRYER FOR POWER TRANSFORMERS. E.B.Franklin. pp.315-18

Elektrichestvo Feb 66
CURRENTS IN PARALLEL BRANCHES OF TRANSFORMER WINDINGS AND REACTORS. (Ru). L.V.Leites.pp.36-41
PERFORMANCE OF AN ELECTRONIC CONVERTOR WITH INTERPHASE TRANSFORMER FOR UNBALANCED GRID CONTROL. (Ru). V.P.Shipillo.pp.42-8
THE ELECTRICAL CHARACTERISTICS FOR THE OIL BARRIER INSULATION OF POWER TRANSFORMERS. (Ru).
D.A.Kaplan et al.pp.66-72
ON POWER RELATIONSHIPS IN RECTIFYING CIRCUITS. (Ru). V.M.Kolesnikov. pp.73-4

RELIABILITY ASSESSMENT OF PROTECTIVE SYSTEMS. A.R.Eames.pp.188-94

Proc.Instn Elect.Engrs Apr 66
LIGHTNING PERFORMANCE OF BRITISH HIGH-VOLTAGE DISTRIBUTION SYSTEMS. R.H.Golde.pp.601-10
SYNTHETIC TESTING OF A.C.CIRCUIT BREAKERS. PART I. METHODS OF TESTING AND RELATIVE SEVERITY. J.G.P.Anderson et al.pp.611-21
WAVE PROPAGATION IN NONHOMOGENEOUS MULTICONDUCTOR SYSTEMS USING THE CONCEPT OF NATURAL MODES. L.M.Wedepohl.pp.622-6
WAVE PROPAGATION IN MULTICONDUCTOR OVERHEAD LINES. CALCULATION OF SERIES IMPEDANCE FOR MULTILAYER EARTH. L.M.Wedepohl et al. pp.627-32
NEW STATIC 3-STEP DISTANCE RELAY. K.Parthasarathy.pp.633-40
THREE-SYSTEM AND SINGLE-SYSTEM STATIC DISTANCE RELAYS. K.Parthasarathy.pp.641-51
A SEASONAL TARIFF FOR DOMESTIC SUPPLIES.* G.B.Lincolne.pp.704-5

Rev.Electrodec.Jul-Aug 65
LONG DISTANCE ELECTRIC POWER TRANSMISSION AND THE SCHEME.FOR TRANSMISSION FROM THE CHOCON-CERROS COLORADOS AREA TO THE COAST (ARGENTINA). (Sp). O.V.Delfino pp.136-49

Technol.Rep.Tohoku Univ.No.2,65
A NEW PROTECTIVE STATIC-RELAY APPLYING FERRITE CORES WITH LOW CURIE TEMPERATURE. K.Murakami et al.pp.233-42
TRANSMISSION THEORY OF PARALLEL

FIG. 20. *Current Papers for the Professional Electrical and Electronics Engineer* (monthly). (By permission of the Institution of Electrical Engineers.)

Modern Materials (*Advances in Development and Applications*) (1958–)

Progress in Cryogenics (1959–)

Advances in Astronomy and Astrophysics (1962–)

Advances in Space Science and Technology (1959–)

Progress in Astronautics and Aeronautics (1960–)

Advances in Information Science and Cybernetics (1966–)

Advances in Mathematics (1961–)

Advances in Magnetic Resonance (1966–)

Solid State Physics (*Advances in Research and Application*) (1955–).

BUTTERWORTH, LONDON

Modern Aspects of Electrochemistry (1954–)

PERGAMON PRESS, OXFORD

Annual Review in Automatic Programming (1960–)

Progress in Materials Science (1949–)

Progress in Aeronautical Science (1961–)

Vistas in Astronomy (1955–).

PLENUM PRESS, NEW YORK

Advances in Electronic Circuit Packaging (1961–)

Advances in Cryogenic Engineering (1955–).

ANNUAL REVIEWS, PALO ALTO, CALIFORNIA

Annual Review of Astronomy and Astrophysics (1963–).

WILEY-INTERSCIENCE, NEW YORK

Advances in Electrochemistry and Electrochemical Engineering (1961–).

GORDON AND BREACH, NEW YORK

Progress in Applied Materials Research (1961–).

Buyers' Guides and Directories

Electrical engineering in all its aspects is exceptionally well provided with directories and buyers' guides. To begin with there are many general trade directories of which *Kelly's Directory of Merchants, Manufacturers and Shippers* (annually) is one of the oldest and most comprehensive. An alphabetical list of firms

Rhodesia and Nyasaland (with the exception of Bulawayo & District).: British & Dominion Eng. (Pvt.) Ltd., P.O. Box 1628, 184 Hatfield Road, Salisbury, Southern Rhodesia.

Bruce Webb (Pvt.) Limited, P.O. Box 1419, 4/5 Scottish Union Building, 64 Abercorn Street, Bulawayo. (Bulawayo & District only).

Tanganyika and Zanzibar: Enfield Cables (Tanganyika) Ltd., P.O. Box 2829, Dar-es-Salaam.

Kenya and Uganda: Marryats East Africa Ltd., P.O. Box 1518, Nairobi, Kenya.

(See Advertisement, pages c46 *and* c47).

DOWTY ELECTRICS LTD.

Tewkesbury, Gloucestershire. *Tel.:* Tewkesbury 2383. *Telegrams:* Electrics Tewkesbury Telex. *Dowtys Tewkesbury Telex.*

Member of the Dowty Group

Manufacturers of aircraft and industrial indicators, micro and rotary switches, solenoids, remote control equipment and mining electrical equipment.

DRYSDALE & CO. LTD.

Yoker, Glasgow, W.4. *Tel.:* Scotstoun 1241. *Telex:* 77524. *Bonaccord Glasgow Telex.*

Manufacturers of centrifugal pumps from three gallons a minute to the largest sizes, also concrete volute pumps upwards of 200 000 gallons per minute (910 000 l). Axial flow and mixed flow pumps, rotary gear wheel pumps for oil pumping. Vacuum pumps and steam engine prime movers for driving pumps, generators, etc. Automatic underground sewage stations and aeration plant for river purification. Pumping auxiliaries for all classes of steam and motor ships.

BRANCH OFFICES:

London: Dunster House, Mincing Lane, E.C.3. *Tel.:* Mansion House 1985. *Bonaccord Fen London. Telex No.:* 22556.

Birmingham, 3: Lombard House, Gt. Charles Street. *Tel.:* Central 2431. *Drysdale Birmingham. Telex No.:* 33662.

Manchester: 190 Wellington Road North, Heaton Norris, Stockport. *Tel.:* Heaton Moor 6261/2. *Drysdale Stockport. Telex No.:* 66499.

Newcastle-on-Tyne, 1: Station Chambers, 10 Neville Street. *Tel.:* Newcastle 2-9931/2. *Efficiency Newcastle-on-Tyne. Telex No.:* 53347.

Liverpool, 3: Norman D. Chisholm, Hamilton Buildings, 24 Chapel Street. *Tel.:* Central 2156/7. *Gascon Liverpool.*

Bristol, 1: S. Jones-Frank & Partners, 57 Queen Square. *Tel.:* Bristol 27241.

FIG. 21. *BEAMA Directory*, 1964–5. (By permission of the British Electrical and Allied Manufacturers' Association.)

in the UK and Europe is given together with an A–Z classified trades list. The Federation of British Industries *Register of British Manufacturers* (also annual) lists the products of its member firms. A newer, general trade directory for the United Kingdom is the *Kompass Directory for Great Britain* in 3 volumes of which the first contains indexes to products and services, the second provides details of firms under 30 main groups and many subdivisions, and the third gives company information by location. An ingenious system gives maximum information within reasonable space limits but, as yet, the lists of firms are by no means complete. Other *Kompass Directories* exist for France, Italy, Spain, Belgium/Luxembourg. Each major manufacturing country has its own trade directories. In the United States, *Thomas's Register of American Manufacturers*, published yearly in 5 volumes, is principally arranged by product.

Classified telephone directories, long established, are useful for tracing firms, and the newer, but the rapidly progressing, Telex directories, although more selective, are also worth consulting.

Two annual publications of *The Electrical Journal* are the *Electrical Trades Directory* (the Blue Book) and *Electricity Undertakings of the World* (the Red Book) (now unfortunately discontinued). *Garcke's Manual* published by the Electrical Press is a statistical record of the British electricity and allied manufacturing industries and includes a directory of executive personnel. The British Electrical and Allied Manufacturers' Association produces annually a *BEAMA Directory* (Fig. 21), which is a buyers' guide, and *BEAMA Handbook*, a guide to the organization of BEAMA. Another useful guide is *Mechanical World Electrical Yearbook*, while the *Wireless and Electrical Trader Year Book* (Iliffe) is a legal, technical, and buying guide for the radio, television and domestic electrical industries. One of a series of "Where to Buy" is *Where to Buy Everything Electrical* which covers power plant, domestic appliances, electronic and radio equipment, etc., and has a list of trade names.

Occasionally, information may be sought on Russian and

other east European trade. A new series of directories in English will be of use here. *Soviet Trade Directory* (Flegon Press, 24 Chancery Lane, London, WC 2) is claimed to be the first such guide published anywhere even in Russia and is based on official Russian resources. It gives a list of Russian factories classified by industry and there are similar directories for Czechoslovakia and Rumania.

Other directories such as the *Engineer* (*Buyers' Guide Issue*) (Morgan Bros.), *British Plastics Yearbook* (Iliffe), *Aeroplane Directory of British Aviation* (Temple Press), and *Machinery's Annual Buyers' Guide* (Machinery Ltd.) will contain much of use to the electrical engineer. Directories relating to specific branches of electrical engineering are described in the appropriate chapters.

CICRIS, the Commercial and Technical Library Service (West London) keeps a union list of directories, registers, and yearbooks held by co-operating libraries. Other guides include G. P. Henderson's *Current British Directories*, 5th edn., 1966, and his *Reference Manual of Directories*, an international guide appearing in parts for each country or group of countries, 1957 onwards, but the latter is now discontinued.

There is no shortage of guides and directories for the electronics industry. Two British ones are *Sell's Automation, Electronics, Nuclear Engineering* (Business Dictionaries Ltd.) and *Instruments: Electronics: Automation: Year Book and Buyers' Guide*, published by Morgan Brothers. The latter includes among the more usual features a list of "who buys" — public service buyers. Among United States publications is the *Electronics Buyers' Guide* (a special issue of the journal *Electronics*) published by McGraw-Hill and including a few British and Japanese entries within its 1340 pages; *EEM: Electronic Engineers' Master* (a catalogue and purchasing guide), published by United Technical Publications, New York, and nearly 3000 pages long; and *Electronic News Financial Fact Book and Directory* (Fairchild Publications Inc.), which includes particularly full information on American companies.

Each industrialized country has, of course, its own directories and buyers' guides. For Germany there is *Die Elektrotechnische Industrie und Ihre Helfer* (annually, Darmstadt) and for Japan the *Japan Electronics Buyers' Guide*. Others will be noted in the guides mentioned in Chapter 2. Directories containing data on electronic components, etc., are described in Chapter 9 on tables, etc.

Questions

1. Describe the desirable features of a good periodical using specific titles to illustrate.

2. Discuss the need for abstracting journals and comment on any current shortcomings that seem apparent.

3. What abstracting services are of particular importance in this subject field? Justify your choice.

4. Compare the functions of published indexing services with abstracting services.

5. Examine critically any two directories concerned with electrical engineering.

CHAPTER 7

Organizations and Societies
621.3(06)

A VERY important key to information is a knowledge of the existence of important organizations and of their status and activities. Through these organizations a great deal of authoritative material is published — periodicals, annual reports, research and statistical reports, monographs, data compilations, etc., representing, in the main, the most significant (sometimes the only available) contributions in the subject field. In many cases, they have on their staff specialists in subject knowledge and organized information services which can be of great assistance where information is required that is not easily obtained elsewhere. The range of such bodies in the field of electrical engineering is extremely varied and covers international organizations, both inter-governmental and non-governmental, government departments and research stations, public utilities, learned and professional societies, trade and development associations, and industrial firms.

International Organizations

Among the aims of international bodies, the United Nations in particular, is the development of ways and means for under-privileged nations to attain a higher standard of living and for industrial countries to progress even further by co-operation. Many of the United Nation's publications, therefore, are related to economic development and serve as authoritative sources for statistical and other basic economic information.

Examples:

> Bibliography on industrialization in underdeveloped countries.
> New sources of energy and economic development.
> Fuel and energy resources.
> Rural electrification.
> Situation and future prospects of Europe's electric power supply industry.
> Electric power in Asia and the Far East.
> Energy development in Latin America.

The Technical Assistance Board of the Economic and Social Council is concerned with the development of industry and agriculture in developing nations. It sponsors the secondment of advisory and training experts to these countries, and training facilities abroad. It also co-operates with such Specialized Agencies of the United Nations as the International Atomic Energy Agency (IAEA) and the International Telecommunication Union (ITU).

Through its Scientific Advisory Committee, the United Nations organizes scientific and technical conferences of which the most important convened over recent years have been the three conferences on the Peaceful Uses of Atomic Energy — 1955, 1958, and 1964. The organization of such gatherings, involving the translation of many documents and the publication of proceedings (17 volumes for 1955; 33 volumes for 1958) is a monumental task beyond the means and ability of any other authority.

Closely associated activities are those of the United Nations Educational, Scientific, and Cultural Organization (Unesco), which works through other agencies for the performance of important tasks. Where no suitable international agency exists, one is created, e.g. the Union of International Engineering

Organizations, the membership of which includes a number of bodies specializing in electrical engineering fields.

Another inter-governmental agency related to the United Nations is the International Bank for Reconstruction and Development (IBRD) and its affiliate, the International Development Association (IDA). The World Bank attaches considerable importance to the role of electric power in economic development. Of the 340 or more development loans made since its formation in 1946 up to mid-1963 totalling 6500 million dollars, 36 per cent was allocated for electric power projects, the largest single category. Projects proposed for financial backing have to be financially, economically, and technically viable. To demonstrate this viability a considerable amount of research has to be done which appears finally in report form. Although a large number of these are staff reports and are restricted to member countries, a number of useful publications are more freely available: annual reports, summary proceedings of annual meetings, booklets and speeches, and press releases. Examples of characteristic publications likely to be of interest:

> Economic comparison of hydroelectric projects with alternative developments of thermal electric power, 1963.
> Electric power regulation in Latin America, 1959.
> Financing of electric power development considerations by IBRD, 1963.

Bibliographical Guides

> United Nations Publications, 1945–63.
> United Nations. Books in Print (annual).
> United Nations Documents Index (monthly).

Separate lists of publications may also be obtained from the individual agencies, e.g. *Publications in the Nuclear Sciences*, 1965, from the IAEA, a bibliography that extends to 99 pages and has many of its entries annotated.

More regionalized, but still inter-governmental, is the Organization for Economic Co-operation and Development first formed by sixteen European countries to make the fullest collective use of individual national capacities and later extended (1961) to cover the promotion of economic growth and financial stability and the development of world economy with particular emphasis on underdeveloped countries. Electric energy, nuclear energy, and automation are three important technological fields embraced by the Organization in its work. Publications appear either as statistical surveys or as technical reports. Exploitation of nuclear energy is carried out separately by the European Nuclear Energy Agency.

Bibliographical Guide

> OECD. General Catalogue of Books; with annual supplements.

Following the best tradition of international communication, valuable contributions to technological advancement are also being made by numerous specialist organizations, some of which are inter-governmental, others are on a less official basis. Encouragement in the use of safety standards at a worldwide level, for instance, is the responsibility of the International Organization for Standardization (ISO); its affiliate in the electrical field is the International Electrotechnical Commission (see Chapter 4).

Important to scientists is the International Union of Pure and Applied Physics (IUPAP), Paris, with membership extending to national research organization. Its work is conducted through various specialist commissions covering such aspects as magnetism, solid state physics, spectroscopy, and high-energy nuclear physics. Other commissions are concerned with the problems of handling and disseminating information. The Union is particularly concerned with international co-ordination in the preparation and publication of abstracts, papers, and tables of physical constants. The various aspects of electrical power generation and distribution are the province of the World Power Conference, the International Union of Producers and Distributors of

Electrical Energy, the International Conference on Large Electrical Systems, and others (see Chapter 11). Organizations specializing in electro-technology and communications include the International Commission on Illumination, International Union for Electroheat, and the International Committee of Electro-chemical Thermodynamics (see Chapter 14); the International Telecommunication Union, International Scientific Radio Union, and the International Radio and Television Organization (see Chapter 17).

They all publish in various forms — bulletins, conference proceedings, monographs, etc. — and the information disseminated is usually of great value.

References

Yearbook of International Organizations (1948+), published by the Union of International Associations, Brussels. The Union also publishes, each December, an *Annual Calendar* of forthcoming events, supplemented by a *Monthly Current List of Newly Published Proceedings of International Congresses* — both are a great help in keeping track of the great number of international congresses and conferences that take place each year.

International Scientific Organizations: a guide to their library documentation and information services. Published by the Library of Congress in 1962, this is an indispensable key to activities and publications. The Library also compiles a monthly *World List of Future International Meetings*, Part 1 of which covers Science and Technology. Another useful publication in the same field is *Scientific Meetings*, issued three times a year by the Special Libraries Association. This is a guide (with subject index) to national, regional, and international gatherings.

Also helping the inquirer to keep track of both international and national conferences that have already taken place and appear in print is the *Index of Conference Proceedings received by the National Lending Library*, Boston Spa, Yorkshire. Introduced in 1965 and published quarterly, this index is intended primarily for identification and loan procedure. Entries are necessarily brief and a keyword index serves as a guide to subject coverage.

International Guide to Sources of Technical Information, published by the OECD (1957), is arranged in subject order and covers European research establishments, standards institutes, university laboratories, etc.

Government Organizations

Government participation in research since 1916 has developed substantially in Great Britain, and very much more so in the United States. In Britain, work involving electrical engineering is carried out by the Post Office, the National Engineering Laboratory, the National Physical Laboratory, the Radio Research Station, the Royal Radar Establishment, the various Ministry of Defence establishments, e.g. Royal Aircraft Establishment, Services Electronics Research Laboratory, Services Valve Test Laboratory, Signals Research and Development Establishment; by the government-backed public authorities — the British Broadcasting Corporation, British Railways, the Central Electricity Generating Board, and the United Kingdom Atomic Energy Authority; and by the industrial co-operative research associations — the British Scientific Instrument Research Association, the Electrical Research Association, and others covering Heating and Ventilation, Hydromechanics, Production Engineering, and Welding.

The number of scientific and technical reports, memoranda, and notes issued by these various bodies are considerable and many of them are likely to be of value in an inquiry. Some may represent the only work done on a particular subject. Unfortunately, some are restricted in their circulation by government or commercial security considerations, others may be available but their existence is not generally made known.

A small number which are on sale at HMSO are listed in *Government Publications* daily and monthly lists (with annual cumulations) and in the special Sectional Lists of HMSO.

Information about unrestricted atomic energy reports appears monthly in the *List of Publications Available to the Public*, issued by the Atomic Energy Research Establishment at Harwell. Some reports are also included in *British National Bibliography*. Another useful publication which covers foreign and domestic reports is the bulletin *R & D Abstracts* produced monthly by the Ministry of Aviation (TIL). An "unclassified" version has been issued since 1962 and should not be difficult to obtain. The National Lending Library introduced in January 1966 a current awareness service listing United Kingdom research reports not normally notified elsewhere.

Most of the establishments mentioned also issue an annual report which constitutes a useful summary of all the significant work done during the year. In addition, separate lists of publications may be freely available.

The importance of such information cannot be over-emphasized and it is desirable, if literature searches are to be thorough, to know of these organizations and their activities. A very useful publication in this respect, also covering academic bodies and industry, is:

> *Industrial Research in Britain*, 5th edn., edited by A. W. HASLETT. Harrap, 1964.

Other useful references:

> *Special Libraries and Information Services in the UK*, 2nd edn., by JACK BURKETT. Library Association, 1965.
> *Technical Services for Industry*. Ministry of Technology, 1966.

US Government participation in scientific and technological research is far greater than that in the United Kingdom and it involves not only civil and defence departments and their laboratories but also a large number of universities and industrial research laboratories working under government contract. Although most of the research is devoted to national defence, there is a constant feed-through to industry, and many new

Field 9/1 – ELECTRONICS AND ELECTRICAL ENGINEERING

properties of the device. Photoresist techniques as employed on this device are discussed. (Author)

AD-625 813   Fld. 9/1
CFSTI Prices: HC $3.00 MF $0.75
BATTELLE MEMORIAL INST COLUMBUS OHIO
MICROELECTRONIC STUDIES. ANALYSIS OF MOSFIELD-EFFECT TRANSISTORS.
Special rept.,
by R. B. Sorkin, J. L. Easterday, J. W. Klapheke, and A. B. Timberlake. 15 Apr 65, 72p. Rept. no. NADC-AE-6513
Task RAV03J004/2021/F021-01-01
Unclassified report

Descriptors: (*Transistors, Microminiaturization (Electronics)). (*Microminiaturization (Electronics), Transistor.), State-of-the art reviews, Integrated circuits, Metals, Oxides, Semiconductors, Performance (Engineering)

The report presents the results of a limited study on the state of the art of MOS field-effect transistors. The study on the MOS field-effect transistors was undertaken to evaluate their potential for integrated circuit applications.

AD-625 831   Fld. 9/1, 13/8
CFSTI Prices: HC $4.00 MF $1.00
BLILEY ELECTRIC CO ERIE PA
PRODUCTION ENGINEERING MEASURE CR-(XM-45)/U CRYSTAL UNITS.

duction samples could be fabricated. Actions which were introduced to resolve these technical difficulties were: submission and approval of a TAR to modify certain SCS-191 requirements (to render the mass loading technique compatible with requirements), mass loading experiments at problem frequencies 5 mc and 16 mc, and fabrication of prototype HC-6/U mounts to accommodate 0.600 inch diameter crystal blanks. Remaining time in the period was expended on fabrication - to the mounting operation of preproduction samples at frequencies 1.75 mc and 10 mc. Although much technical progress has been made, additional design refinements are required at frequencies 5 mc and 6 mc before preproduction samples will be fabricated at these 2 frequencies. (Author)

AD-625 904   Fld. 9/1, 11/7
CFSTI Prices: HC $1.00 MF $0.50
NAVAL RESEARCH LAB WASHINGTON D C
ELECTROMAGNETIC SHIELDING WITH COKE,
by P. F. Nicholson. 18 Jul 60, 17p. Rept. no. NRL-1080
Unclassified report

Descriptors: (*Electromagnetic shielding, Coal), (*Noise, Electromagnetic shielding). (*Coal, Electromagnetic shielding), Materials. Effectiveness, Concrete, Frequency

It was found that a reasonably good grade of high temperature coke satisfied the requirements of an excellent electromagnetic shield plus being both

Descriptors: (*Tunnel (Electronics)), X-band, Methods, Processing, Semiconductor capsulation, Germanium Arsenic, Gallium

The report presents an account tunnel diode improvement results obtained from reliability devices fabricated by the imp new solid structure tunnel di during this contract which exl bility characteristics to any pr nel diode. The process and fa this device along with reliabili in the report. (Author)

AD-625 972   Fld. 9/1
AIR FORCE CAMBRIDGE L G HANSCOM FIELD WAVE PHYSICS LAB
THE SHORT-BACKFIRE ANT
by H. W. Ehrenspeck. 2 Jun 6
Instrumentation Papers-86
Proj: AF-5635   Task 563502
AFCRL 65-768

Availability: Published in I IEEE v53 n8 p1138-40 Aug 1: users only.

Descriptors: (*Antennas,

products come into commercial production because of it. The great number of reports issued (there are some 3000 unrestricted reports per annum covering electronics alone), fortunately, are adequately covered in bibliographical publications.

The Federal Government's special centre for the collection and distribution to the public of the technical reports growing out of research financed by the Army, Navy, Air Force, Atomic Energy Commission, and other Federal Agencies, is the Clearinghouse for Federal Scientific and Technical Information (formerly the Office of Technical Services (OTS)), Washington. It is also the national clearing house for translations and translation information. CFSTI issues the following publications:

> *US Government Research and Development Reports* (Fig. 22), twice a month, announces, indexes and abstracts approximately 2000 new reports of government-sponsored research released each month through CFSTI.
>
> *Technical Reports Newsletter*, aimed primarily at small and medium-sized industries, reviews six to eight new reports each month.
>
> *CFSTI Selective Bibliographies* of reports and translations covering many special areas of considerable interest, include compilations for computers, printed electronic circuits, data processing and programming, ferroelectricity, lasers and masers, magnetohydrodynamics, unconventional power sources, semiconductors, thermoelectricity, transistors, and ultrasonics.

The US Atomic Energy Commission is another clearing house for scientific and technical information with many applications in other fields. In addition to notification through the CFSTI, information on research publications is disseminated through *Nuclear Science Abstracts* (twice a month), *Research and Development Abstracts* (four a year), and *Bibliographies of Interest to the Atomic Energy Program* (TID-3043, Rev. 2), 1962.

Other reports likely to be of use to electrical engineers may

06-10 ELECTRONICS

N66-16021# Hewlett-Packard Co. Palo Alto, Calif.
MICROWAVE POWER MEASUREMENT
Oct. 1965   90 p refs
(HP-AN64)

Instruments and techniques used for microwave power measurements are described. Various types of bolometers, peak power meters, and calorimetric power meters are discussed in detail. General precautions that should be observed when making microwave power measurements are summarized. Practical techniques for measuring average power and peak pulse power are examined. Calibration services available at the NBS and HP standards laboratories are reported. Methods for improving accuracy are suggested. A section is also included on power level control.   M.R.W.

N66-16052*# National Aeronautics and Space Administration. Goddard Space Flight Center, Greenbelt, Md.
GAMMA, ELECTRON, AND PROTON RADIATION EXPO-SURES OF P-CHANNEL, ENHANCEMENT, METAL OXIDE SEMICONDUCTOR, FIELD EFFECT TRANSISTORS
Harry E. Wannemacher   Aug. 1965   50 p refs
(NASA-TM-X-55359; X-716-65-351) CFSTI: HC $2.00/MF $0.50 CSCL 09A

P-channel enhancement MOS insulated gate field effect transistors were irradiated with either Co_{60} gammas, 2 Mev electrons, or 22 Mev protons. These devices experienced

of various tests conducted to appraise their performance. The ASDE-2 was equipped with specially modified modulators for tests of the SFD-315 magnetron. The Solid State Duplexer was operated in an unmodified channel of the radar and performed satisfactorily throughout a life-test period of 2500 hours. It was concluded that satisfactory system performance can not be achieved using the modified modulators provided for operation of the SFD-315 magnetron; however, the SFD-315 magnetron is suitable for ASDE-2 applications with a compatible modulator, and may be expected to operate satisfactorily for more than 5000 hours. It was also concluded that the solid state duplexer is a suitable replacement for the original duplexer of ASDE-2.   Author

N66-16101# Motorola, Inc., Phoenix, Ariz.   Semiconductor Products Div.
HIGH SPEED SEMICONDUCTOR SWITCH (TWO TERMI-NAL) AND HIGH SPEED SEMICONDUCTOR SWITCH (GATE) Ninth Quarterly Report. 29 May–29 Aug. 1965
B. G. Burlingame 28 Aug. 1965 19 p
(Contract DA-36-039-AMC-01475(E))
(QR-9; AD-624153) CFSTI: HC $1.00/MF $0.50

Results are given that were obtained from the use of higher gold diffusion temperatures and a decrease in starting material resistivity, as well as a change in geometry of the three-terminal die. Changes in measurement techniques and conditions are discussed. Summaries of device characteristics

Fig. 23. *Scientific and Technical Aerospace Reports (STAR).* (By permission of the National Aeronautics and Space Administration, Washington.)

emanate from the National Aeronautics and Space Administration. These are listed fortnightly in *NASA Scientific and Technical Aerospace Reports* (*STAR*) (Figs. 23 and 24) and cumulate in the annual *Index of NASA Technical Publications*. Additional information about US Government reports and other forms of publication is available in the *Monthly Catalog of United States Government Publications*. *The Government-Wide Index to Federal Research and Development Reports* is a monthly guide NSA, STAR, USGRDR and the *Technical Abstract Bulletin*.

Electrical Engineering Societies

Promotion of the exchange of ideas and the advancement of knowledge have been the aims of societies ever since the seventeenth century when the Royal Society (1660) and the French Academy of Sciences (1666) were formed. The more specialized professional society mainly came into being during the nineteenth century, for example the Institution of Mechanical Engineers in 1847, the Institution of Electrical Engineers in 1871, and the Physical Society in 1847. In the United States the American Society of Mechanical Engineers was formed in 1880, the Institute of Electrical and Electronic Engineers in 1884, and the American Physical Society in 1899.

With the rapid growth of electrical engineering as a major technology, certain sections developed to become important technologies in their own right and societies were formed to represent the workers in them. Thus were formed the Illuminating Engineering Society in New York in 1906 and its London counterpart in 1909; the Association of Public Lighting Engineers in 1928; the Electrochemical Society, New York, in 1902; the Institute of Radio Engineers, New York, in 1912; the Institution of Electronic and Radio Engineers, London, in 1925; and the Television Society, London, in 1927.

All societies have the purpose of promoting knowledge in their respective fields by meetings, discussion, publications, and a library service. Generally speaking, membership includes scientists and engineers of repute and others with developing

SUBJECT INDEX

FIG. 24. Index of *Scientific and Technical Aerospace Reports*.

skills. The society publications, therefore, reflect this high level of attainment, and are regarded as primary sources of information.

References

> *Scientific and Learned Societies of Great Britain*, Allen & Unwin (for the British Council). Frequently revised, this excellent publication serves as a guide to the objects, membership, and activities of over 900 different societies arranged in 16 sections.
>
> *Encyclopedia of Associations*, Gale, Detroit, 4th edn., 1964. Volume 1 covers national organizations of the United States.
>
> *Scientific and Technical Societies of the United States and Canada*, Washington, National Academy of Sciences — National Research Council, 7th edn., 1961. Arranged in alphabetical order, Part I covers US organizations and Part II Canada. There is also a subject index.
>
> *Scientific Societies in the United States* by R. S. BATES, 2nd edn., Oxford University Press, 1958.
>
> *Europa Year Book*. Europa Publications, London, annual. Under each country information is included on societies, libraries, academic bodies, etc. Volume 1 covers Europe, and volume 2 Africa, the Americas, Asia and Australasia. Under French Trade and Industry, for example, details are given about the Syndicat Général des Industries de la Construction Electrique including the fact that it publishes a monthly journal *La Construction Electrique*.

Specifically concerned with Russia is the *Directory of Selected Scientific Institutions in the USSR* prepared by the National Science Foundation and published by Merrill Books, Inc., Columbus in January 1963. Organizations are arranged alphabetically but there is a detailed subject index and a keyword-in-title index of institutions. There is an entry, for example, under Electrical Engineering Institute of Communications, Moscow.

The main entry indicates that it is an academic body and describes the nature of equipment and extent and form of training.

Far wider geographical coverage is given by the *World of Learning* (London, Europa) although the information given is quite brief. Under France — Academies and Learned Societies, for example, we find the Société Française des Electriciens (CSSF), founded in 1883, with 6200 members and publishing regularly a *Bulletin*. Under Research Institutes is the Centre National de la Recherche Scientifique including a list of its various research centres.

Important Publishing Activities

The Institution of Electrical Engineers has a heavy publishing programme that covers periodicals for different readership requirements; three abstracting journals; a number of books and pamphlets on topics such as components, valves and semiconductors, radio and television, aircraft and aviation, communication, education, automation and computers, and wiring diagrams; and various conference and symposia proceedings (list of publications on sale available).

Periodical publications include:

The monthly *Proceedings of the IEE*.
Electronics and Power, the monthly journal of the Institution.
Students Quarterly Journal.
IEE News, a monthly tabloid newspaper.
Electronics Letters (monthly), a rapid means of communicating new information and results on important topics of current interest.

The important abstracting and indexing services *Science Abstracts*, *Current Papers*, and the new fortnightly *Current Papers in Physics* (from mid November, 1965), are discussed in Chapter 6, together with *Current Papers on Control*.

The Institute of Electrical and Electronic Engineers, New York, has as its aims the advancement of the theory and practice of electrical engineering, electronics, radio, allied branches of engineering or the related arts and sciences. Apart from the annual convention, general meetings, regional conventions, and conferences, within the IEE structure are 31 groups representing specialist interests, each with its own transactions and newsletter. Examples of subjects covered are aerospace, automatic control, broadcasting, circuit theory, computers, education, engineering management, industrial electronics, information theory, microwave technology, power, etc.

Periodical publications include:

> *Proceedings of the IEEE* (monthly) for advanced papers.
>
> *IEEE Transactions* (quarterly or bi-monthly) representing the specialized groups.
>
> *IEEE Spectrum* (monthly), intended for a wider readership,
>
> *IEEE Student Journal* (bi-monthly), providing career information and educational material of a technical, scientific, or professional nature.
>
> The annual *IEEE International Convention Record*, standards developed by technical committees, and various special publications.

The activities of two closely related organizations — the Physical Society and the American Physical Society — should also be followed, particularly for developments in electron, plasma, and solid state physics. The same applies to the two great engineering bodies — the Institution of Mechanical Engineers and the American Society of Mechanical Engineers.

Industrial Organizations

Many of the large and medium-sized firms engaged in electrical engineering have impressive research facilities and a great deal of information is generated from them. For current awareness, of course, much of this information is unobtainable immediately because of industrial security. Nevertheless, a lot of useful data eventually becomes freely available through reports, house journals, articles contributed to professional and commercial periodicals, patents, brochures, and data sheets.

Every manufacturing company disseminates information on its products through trade catalogues, many of which constitute first-class sources of technical data. Fewer, however, are engaged in other publication activities. The house journal is the most important medium for communication and, in many cases, the articles in them are worthwhile contributions. In some cases lists of company technical reports are included.

Industrial organizations making useful contributions to published knowledge include AEI Ltd., English Electric, GEC, British Insulated Callender's Cables, ICT Ltd., Muirhead, Mullard, Parsons, Pye, etc. In Europe are the important firms Allgemeine Elektricitäts-Gesellschaft (AEG), Allamania Svenska Elektriska Aktiebologet (ASEA), Ateliers de Constructions Electriques de Charleroi (ACEC), Keuring van Elektrotechnische Materials (KEMA), and Philips of Eindhoven.

Important firms in the United States distributing information include Alco Products, Allis Chalmers, Atomics International, Babcock & Wilcox, Bell Telephone Laboratories, General Dynamics, General Electric, and Westinghouse.

For tracing industrial activities in Europe important publications are: Haslett's *Research in Britain*; G. P. Henderson's *European Companies: a guide to sources of information*, London, CBD Research Ltd., 1962; and *Industrial European Guide: steel, engineering, nucleonics*, 1965–6, Darmstadt, H. F. Jaeger KG, in English, French, and German.

For the USA there are two very good guides. *Industrial Research Laboratories of the United States*, compiled by J. H. Gribbin and S. S. Krogfus, 12th edn., New York, Bowker, 1965, gives such details as subjects of research, and the names and numbers of research staff. Entries are arranged alphabetically; where big companies are involved there is a breakdown to Divisions. *Specialized Scientific Information Services in the US*, Washington, National Science Foundation, 1961, which lists over 400 different organizations or projects, outlines the scope of their work, what material is collected, the information services provided, and the type of publication issued.

The names of firms specializing in different products can be located from trade directories and buyers' guides (see Chapter 6).

Questions

1. Describe the functions, activities, and publications of any one international organization making an important contribution in your particular subject field.

2. Comment on the value of the research report as a means of communication and list the most useful bibliographical tools that can be used to trace them.

3. Select a significant branch of electrical engineering and trace current research in progress, naming organizations involved. List the information sources used.

4. Compare the publishing output of United Kingdom government research establishments with comparable organizations in the United States in one specific subject area.

5. Discuss the importance of publications emanating from conferences and congresses and suggest methods that might be used to trace their existence and contents.

CHAPTER 8

Studying Electrical Engineering
UDC 621.3(07)

Higher Training

IN SPITE of the excellent facilities that exist for advanced education in electrical and electronic engineering and good career prospects, the number of applications for university places in technology are proportionally far lower than for other courses. According to *Education* for 22 February 1963, for the academic year 1963/4 there was only one applicant per place as compared with at least two per place for other courses. The reason appears to stem partly from a common sixth-form conception that the technologist is not far removed from the technician and is concerned with purely mechanical tasks. The scientist, on the other hand, is considered to be a person apart doing work that leads constantly to new discoveries and great prestige.

Good engineering facilities offered by the universities, and the recent university status granted to colleges of advanced technology, will no doubt help to correct this unfortunate impression. The technologist, of course, is a trained scientist applying scientific method and approach to engineering problems. His job is both intellectual and administrative — he develops ideas and ensures that they are carried through to the working stage.

The student in fact spends much of his time in elaborating the mathematics and physics taken in the sixth form. A characteristic first-degree course of 3 years, for example, will probably cover physics, chemistry, and mathematics in the first year, with specialization starting in the second. Initially, the syllabus will

104

be concerned with establishing principles rather than techniques; design and laboratory work follows later. In many instances the student is sent out to industry to work during each of his summer vacation periods. Such training, of course, is insufficient to equip the undergraduate as an engineer. Some graduates, therefore, serve a 2-year period of training in industry after taking their degree. Alternatively, they may spend a year in industry before going to university and a year after academic training.

The Diploma of Technology courses in Engineering (now recognised as degree courses) differ from full-time degree courses by stipulating periods of training in industry as part of the qualification. These sandwich courses as they are called are offered by most of the colleges of advanced technology (now of university status) and a number of colleges of technology, the apportionment of industrial experience varying from place to place. Students may spend 6 months in industry followed by 6 months in study. Alternatively, 1 year may be spent in industry prior to a 3–4-year course of continuous study, followed by a further year in industry. Where the college arranges the training students go to different firms for each of the training periods. Industrial-sponsored students return each period for training to the firm to which they are tied.

The syllabus also includes management aspects, human studies, and places great emphasis in the final year on project work. At the conclusion of the course a student should be reasonably well equipped to understand the interaction between design, construction, operation, and maintenance problems. He should have learnt something, too, of the relationships between professional electrical engineers and others engaged in modern industry.

Higher National Diploma courses offered by certain colleges of technology are generally full-time or industry-based sandwich courses, closely associated with the requirements of the Institution of Electrical Engineers or the Institution of Electronic and Radio Engineers. All courses run for 3 years, with an additional fourth year leading to the college diploma and to meet the educational requirements of the appropriate professional body.

Research

Most universities and colleges also provide facilities for post-graduate research covering between them electronics, radio and telecommunications, control engineering, computing, electric power engineering and machinery, and nuclear engineering. Birmingham University, for instance, is primarily concentrating on echo-ranging systems, circuits, computers, solid-state electronics, etc.; Southampton on quantum electronics, microwave electronics, low-frequency circuit applications, etc.; and Sheffield on microwave and millimetre wave studies. (See *NERC Review* (January 1965 onwards) for the series Electronics Research in British Universities covering Birmingham, Southampton, Sheffield North Wales, and Liverpool. University research is also summarized annually in a publication from HMSO.)

Choice of College

Information on entrance requirements, scope of courses, duration, student facilities, and other matters is fully covered in the prospectus issued by individual teaching establishments. For Great Britain a useful summary guide to universities, colleges of advanced technology, technical colleges, and industrial scholarships is *Which University?*, revised by D. Lambert (London, Cornmarket Press, 1966). Wider in scope is the *Commonwealth Universities Yearbook*, published by the Association of Universities of the British Commonwealth, London.

The United States is covered by the *New American Guide to Colleges* by Gene R. Hawes (Columbia University Press, 1962) and *American Universities and Colleges*, published by the American Council on Education, Washington.

In the engineering fields, employers pay close attention to the form and standard of teaching at the different establishments as an important criterion for personnel selection. The activities of the Engineers' Council for Professional Development, New York, therefore, are particularly useful. The Council represents the nine large engineering societies, the National Council of

State Boards of Engineering Examiners, and the Engineering Institute of Canada, and its main concern is the approval of curricula for first degree engineering courses. Before acceptance they are thoroughly considered by a competent committee of engineers and engineering educators. The resultant publication, *Curricula Leading to First Degrees in Engineering (Accredited)*, lists all institutions which have met the Council's standards. Revised annually, it is taken by many organizations and corporations as a basis for accepting applicants for employment.

Briefer information but with worldwide scope is *World of Learning*, which lists by country the various teaching establishments and the different faculties available, names of teaching staff, and publications. Also useful is the *International Handbook of Universities*, published by the International Association of Universities, Paris.

Many students may be anxious to continue their study at postgraduate level; others may wish to seek facilities not available in their own countries. For these Unesco publishes regularly a directory of officially sponsored programmes entitled *Study Abroad*.

Teaching Methods

On the question of curricula most teachers will design their own teaching programmes and favour particular textbooks. It is helpful, however, to examine the methods being used in other teaching establishments particularly at a time when so many changes are taking place. A useful book in this respect is F. Slaughter's *Design and the Education of Mechanical Engineering*, Pitman, 1963. It is a survey of some of the most important engineering schools in the world and a study of the changing pattern of approach and teaching philosophy. The occasional conference reports of the Engineering Societies of Western Europe and the United States, *On Education and Training of Professional Engineers*, are worthy of attention in this respect.

An interesting appraisal of Diploma of Technology courses

has been made by Marie Jahoda in *The Education of Technologists* (London, Tavistock Publications, 1963). This exploratory case study at Brunel College examines sandwich courses in detail, including syllabus experience and student reactions.

An important publication that looks at the problem of broadening the education of would-be technologists by the introduction of non-scientific subjects is *The Complete Scientist*, prepared by the Leverhulme Study Group for the British Association for the Advancement of Science (Oxford University Press, 1961). It considers as a whole the successive stages in the education of the future graduate scientist and engineer from lower forms of grammar schools to postgraduate courses.

The problems faced by the smaller firm so far as technical training is concerned are the subject of *The Smaller Firm and Technical Education* by P. F. R. Venables and W. J. Williams (London, Max Parrish, 1961). An older work that may still be useful is H. R. Mill's *Techniques of Technical Training* (London, Cleaver-Hume, 1953).

A useful American guide for the teacher, although it covers all subjects, is *Textbooks in Print* (annual), including related teaching materials (New York, Bowker).

Theses

The university thesis, like the research report, describes research work and its results, but its main purpose is to prove the ability of the student to organize a systematic investigation. Some of the data included might well be of value to an inquirer, but in most cases it has to be sifted from a considerable amount of other detail before it can be made useful . Nevertheless, the thesis cannot be ignored as a promising source of information. It may report on a facet of research that coincides with that of the inquirer and has not been reported elsewhere.

In Great Britain the availability of university theses varies considerably. Some are only available for reference in the university or departmental library; some may be photocopied or borrowed. In other instances the permission of the author

ENGINEERING AND TECHNOLOGY

3316. DARWENT, T. J. (LWestC). Numerical solution of elliptic partial differential equations for neutron flux in a reactor. M.Sc.

3317. MENELEY, D. A. (LIC). Experimental studies of neutron diffusion in the presence of absorbers and voids. PH.D.

3318. ROSHD, M. H. M. (LCCST). A critical survey of the physics of the spectral shift control reactor. [Diss.] M.SC.

3319. SMYTHE, W. D. (LIC). Experimental studies of anisotropic neutron diffusion in graphite lattices. M.SC.

3320. ANDERSON, D. (M). Design and kinetics study of an advanced gas-cooled reactor. M.SC.

3321. ECCLESTONE, M. J. (O, *Wadham*). Monte Carlo methods applied to atomic reactor problems. B.SC.

Electrical Engineering

See also Control Engineering, p. 162.

Electric Machines. Transformers

3322. DORWARD, L. F. (A). Control of the speed of induction motors by means of mercury-vapour triodes. PH.D.

3323. HARAN, N. A. W. (B). Speed control of an induction motor by using rotor switches. M.SC.

3324. NOBLE, A. E. (B). An experimental investigation of magnetic noise in small dynamos. M.SC.

and head of department has to be obtained before access is possible. Notification of existence is not normally as speedy as in the United States or France. The main key in this country is the Aslib *Index to Theses accepted for Higher Degrees in the Universities of Great Britain and Ireland*, published annually (Fig. 25). Details of theses and dissertations can also be obtained separately from each university. The London University, for instance, publishes a printed catalogue complete with indexes of authors and subjects. The current list includes over 20 titles on specific aspects of electrical engineering submitted to the University College, Imperial College, Northampton College of Advanced Technology, King's College, Queen Mary College, and Battersea College of Technology.

To speed up notification the National Electronics Research Council are listing in their quarterly *NERC Review* British university theses of interest to electronics research workers. Over 200 theses accepted by 32 universities and colleges were listed in the April 1965 issue.

The main notification service in the United States is the monthly *Dissertation Abstracts* (Fig. 26), published by University Microfilms Inc. The many titles recorded, representing over 160 universities and colleges, are available in microform and xerox. An annual publication is *American Doctoral Dissertations* available as an extra.

Useful as a retrospective bibliography is L. M. Marckworth's *Dissertations in Physics*, produced by IBM's San Jose Laboratory and published by the Stanford University Press, 1961. Supported by 97 universities it serves as an index to more than 8400 titles written between 1861 and 1959. In addition to specifically physics degrees, related disciplines such as electrical engineering topics are also included. Part II of this bibliography is a machine-processed subject index based on keywords.

French theses are listed in a separate catalogue issued as a supplement to *Bibliographie de la France*. Copies of theses announced can be obtained from the Centre National de la Recherche Scientifique in Paris.

ENGINEERING

6474

HARMONIC GENERATION IN HCN
BY MULTIPLE QUANTUM CONVERSION

(Order No. 65-3165)

Donald Paul Akitt, Ph.D.
University of Illinois, 1964

An experiment in harmonic generation by a travelling wave, multiple photon interaction in HCN gas is presented. The $J = 0$, $J = 1$ rotational levels of HCN are used to multiply from 34.7 Gc to 104 Gc with a peak power output at 104 Gc in excess of 1.5 watts.

The theory of third harmonic generation in a two level quantum system is discussed. Approximate solutions for the harmonic polarization terms are obtained and the magnitude of the third harmonic power is evaluated in terms of known parameters of the quantum system and the electromagnetic circuit. The theoretical predictions and experimental results are found to be in close agreement.

Details of the simple rectangular waveguide interaction region and coupling structure are discussed.

The application of the nonlinear interaction to the generation of sub-millimeter waves is considered.

Microfilm $2.75; Xerography $3.60. 64 pages.

equations to the case where the design specifications are given in terms of a desired transfer function matrix rather than a desired time solution. This extension yields matrix equations in A, B, C and D which provide necessary and sufficient conditions for a state model to be equivalent to a specified transfer function matrix.

The fundamental design equations can be programmed directly on the digital computer. This leads immediately to a computer technique for parameter optimization. The least squared-error criteria is used together with the method of steepest descent to achieve optimization. A computer program implementing this technique is included. Several examples are included which illustrate the design and optimization methods.

Microfilm $2.75; Xerography $5.40. 109 pages.

THE DRIVING-POINT IMPEDANCE
OF AN ELECTRICALLY SHORT CYLINDRICAL
ANTENNA IN THE IONOSPHERE.

(Order No. 65-4042)

Fig. 26. *Dissertation Abstracts.* (By permission of University Microfilms Inc., Ann Arbor, Mich.)

Questions

1. Make a list of research work that is being done by British universities in the field of electrical engineering.

2. Compile a bibliography of US theses submitted within the past 5 years covering any one important branch of electrical engineering.

3. Comment on and evaluate the various bibliographical services that can be used in tracing university theses in Europe, Britain, and the United States.

CHAPTER 9

Tables, Statistics, Patents, Trade Marks, Trade Literature
UDC 621.3(08)

Tables

THE electrical engineer often needs precise data of a mathematical, physical, or engineering nature, and there are many publications available for him to use. Some are more authoritative than others, and those that have been issued or sponsored by learned societies or other institutions may be regarded as completely reliable. Most publications of this type issued in other ways, however, are authentic, and notes of a selection of these are given below. For an evaluation of new publications in this field, readers are advised to consult critical reviews in the periodical literature.

General Mathematical and Physical Tables

Probably the best known of all tables are the National Academy of Sciences, National Research Council (USA) — *International Critical Tables of Numerical Data of Physics, Chemistry and Technology*, published 1926–33 by McGraw-Hill in 7 volumes and an index. A German compilation which has been successively revised is H. H. Landolt and R. Börnstein, *Zahlenwerte und Funktionen aus Physik, Chemie, Astronomie, Geophysik und Technik*, Springer Verlag, 1950–63. This is issued in a number of volumes of which several deal with electrical properties, magnetic properties, electrical techniques, and so on. Refer-

113

ences are made to the original sources of the data. No new complete revised editions will appear in future, however, but a series of individual works will be published and revised as necessary.

Of more modest proportions but still very useful is *Tables of Physical and Chemical Constants, and some Mathematical Functions* by G. W. C. Kaye and T. H. Laby, 13th edn., Longmans, 1966. *Chambers' Seven-figure Mathematical Tables*, ed. by J. Pryde, 1958, is another shorter work of particular value to students, as is *Barlow's Tables of Squares, Cubes, Square Roots, Cube Roots, and Reciprocals of all Integers up to 12,500* by P. Barlow (ed. by L. J. Comrie), London, Spon, 1941. *Mathematical Tables* of the British Association for the Advancement of Science under the auspices of the Royal Society were published by the Cambridge University Press in 10 volumes between 1931 and 1952. The Smithsonian Institution, Washington, is responsible for several useful data compilations including *Smithsonian Physical Tables*, ed. by W. E. Forsythe, 1954 (9th edn.), and *Smithsonian Logarithmic Tables to Base e and Base 10*, 1952.

Specialized Tables

A series of *Tables of Constants and Numerical Data* has been in publication by Pergamon since 1947 and each volume includes full references. One example is *Magnetic (Faraday) and Magneto Optic (Kerr) Rotation* by R. de Mallemann and F. Suhner (vol. 3 of the series), published in 1951.

A French work of particular interest is *Notes et Formulas de l'Ingenieur:* Tome 4, *Électronique appliquée, Télécommunication, Électronique, Électroacoustique, Électricité, Traction Électrique* by M. Denis-Papin and J. Vallot, Paris, Michel, 1955. Wiley have published (1964) *Elphyma Tables: tables, formulas, nomograms within mathematics–physics–electricity* by E. Ingelstam and S. Sjoberg, a very practical collection of data for both the student and practising engineer.

Other works include *Engineering Units and Physical Quantities* by H. S. Hvistendahl, London, Macmillan, 1964; *The Funda-*

mental Constants of Physics by E. R. Cohen and others, New York, Interscience, 1957; *Wavelength Tables with Intensities in Arc, Spark or Discharge Tubes*, by G. R. Harrison, Wiley, 1939; and *Technical Data on Fuel*, ed. by H. M. Spiers, 6th edn., London, the British National Committee, World Power Conference, 1961.

For mathematical functions outside the more basic tables the National Physical Laboratory has published a series of *Mathematical Tables* (HMSO, 1956–60, 4 vols.) of which the first title is mainly concerned with the *Use and Construction of Mathematical Tables* by L. Fox.

Many data books for highly specialized subject areas are available. For example, the Radio Research Laboratories of the Ministry of Postal Services, Tokyo, have issued an *Atlas of Radio Wave Propagation Curves for Frequencies between 30 and 10,000 Mc/s* (1957). The firm of Johnson, Matthey & Co. Ltd., issue a number of *Electrical Engineering Data Sheets* which together form their Catalogue No. 1300. The emphasis is on metals and other materials for electrical engineering. Many other firms issue data books: just two examples are Gilby-Brunton's *Resistance Handbook* and the *Electrical Alloy Data Book* of the British Driver Harris Co. Ltd.

Bibliographies of Tables

Several bibliographies serve as useful guides to the tables in existence and show where there are gaps and where there are already sufficient compilations. *Guide to Tables in Mathematical Statistics* by J. A. Greenwood and H. O. Hartley, published by the Princeton University Press in 1962, was sponsored by the National Research Council and analyses the contents of books of tables. It has author and subject indexes. *Index of Mathematical Tables* by A. Fletcher and others was first published in 1946 and revised and enlarged in 1961. The later edition is in 3 parts (in 2 vols.): Part 1 describes the tables according to function, Part 2 is a bibliography of tables according to author and Part 3 lists known errors in published tables. *Guide to Mathematical Tables* by A. V. Lebedev and R. M. Fedorova, Pergamon Press, 1960, is translated from the Russian, and although international in scope is naturally particularly strong on Russian tables. There is a *Supplement No. 1* by N. M. Buronova, Pergamon, 1960, which brings the work up to 1958 and adds some items missed by the original compilers. The *Index of Mathematical Tables* by Karl Schütte, Munich, Oldenbourg, 1955, is in German and English and is arranged by subject with author and institutional indexes. The Royal Society has prepared a "List of Compendia and Data Tables in Physics" which was published in *Journal of Documentation*, **7** (4) 252–5 (December 1951).

Energy and Production Statistics

Electrical Energy Supply

Planning for future energy requirements and estimating the demand for electrical equipment, both for internal and overseas markets, depends on reliable statistics such as those compiled by international organizations and by the various national official bodies. The World Power Conference saw the need for a systematic approach and published a series of *Statistical Year-books* from 1936 to 1960. The United Nations, however, in 1952 started a similar service and, to avoid duplicating effort, the Conference in 1962 commenced a new series *Survey of Energy Resources* covering data not dealt with elsewhere. With revision every 6 years, information is given on: national resources of various primary fuels, water power, and the oxides of uranium and thorium, the basic fuel for nuclear power.

The J Series of Statistical Papers, initiated by the United Nations in 1952, entitled *World Energy Supplies*, presents in country order figures for the annual production, trade and consumption of various solid, liquid, and gaseous forms of energy and electricity. The series covers the years from 1929:

1929–50, 1951–4, 1955–8, 1958–61, etc. Useful statistics on world electricity production are also included in the United Nations *Monthly Bulletin of Statistics* and the *Statistical Yearbook*. Indications to the future requirements of underprivileged countries may be found in the various reports of the International Bank for Reconstruction and Development and in some of the papers read at various meeting and conferences of the World Power Conference.

More specifically for Europe is *Basic Statistics of Energy* published by the OECD and covering 18 different European countries, the United States, and Canada. The latest edition covers the years 1952–63. Since Japan became an OECD member in 1964, later editions will include statistics from that country. OECD also publishes an annual *Electricity Industry Survey*, Part 1 of which is a general review of the supply industry in OECD countries including forecasts for 5 years ahead, and Part 2 statistical tables for member countries. From the United Nations comes the *Quarterly Bulletin of Electrical Energy Statistics for Europe* showing, country by country, production (thermal, hydro, nuclear, etc.), international exchanges, and gross consumption. Captions and headings are printed in English, French, and Russian. Also looking at Europe is the monthly *General Statistical Bulletin* of the European Economic Community which includes tables of electrical output for each of the countries within its control.

A useful compilation for statistical comparison is *International Statistics of Electrical Energy Generation and Consumption*, published annually since 1926 by the international organization Unipede, in Paris.

Greater detail, of course, is available from the annual reports of each country's major power producers, the annual reports of the Electricity Council and the Central Electricity Generating Board (HMSO) being very good examples. Also useful for its concise presentation of generating data is the *Monthly Digest of Statistics* (HMSO) (Fig. 27).

Data concerning the world's electricity power producers,

J

ELECTRONIC APPARATUS

TABLE 80

Deliveries of electronic apparatus(¹)

£ thousand

	Electronic control equipment(²)		Electronic computers		Electronic measuring and testing equipment(³)		Transmitters(⁴)		Radar and navigational aids		Radio communication equipment		All other electronic apparatus(⁵)	
	Total	For export	Total	For export	Total	For export	Total	For export	Total	For export	Total	For export	Total	For export
1960	3,169	340	8,196	2,301	10,893	3,741	4,360	2,828	14,619	9,875	11,535	7,531	7,129	3,139
1961	11,918	3,142	10,903	1,262	11,652	3,890	5,478	3,097	14,059	9,056	13,406	8,645	9,871	4,568
1962	15,384	3,904	13,440	2,544	13,963	4,186	6,374	3,780	18,121	11,998	15,677	10,020	9,164	3,839
1963	16,909	5,663	24,752	3,526	13,392	4,626	5,816	3,260	25,017	18,603	13,914	8,929	12,910	4,360
1964	14,953	4,537	44,164	4,960	15,375	4,627	8,695	5,474	66,224	21,513	30,732	11,896	23,233	5,964
1963 1st qtr.	4,450	1,380	6,105	622	3,074	992	1,111	595	5,699	4,112	3,620	2,379	3,092	917
2nd qtr.	3,823	1,567	4,082	893	3,291	1,149	1,102	588	5,683	4,375	3,376	2,072	3,187	1,101
3rd qtr.	3,925	1,286	7,232	1,460	3,603	1,352	1,495	932	5,673	3,980	3,234	2,054	3,205	1,072
4th qtr.	4,712	1,430	7,333	552	3,424	1,133	2,108	1,145	7,962	6,136	3,714	2,425	3,425	1,270
1964 1st qtr.	3,895	1,059	11,054	1,236	3,696	1,061	1,975	1,145	16,095	5,085	8,112	3,182	5,773	1,581
2nd qtr.	3,477	1,111	10,233	623	3,733	1,092	2,537	1,592	16,583	5,755	7,352	2,901	5,254	1,346
3rd qtr.	3,237	1,038	11,196	1,044	3,827	1,172	2,206	1,400	16,689	5,471	7,062	2,863	5,773	1,381
4th qtr.	4,344	1,330	11,680	2,057	4,119	1,304	1,982	1,338	16,857	5,203	8,206	2,950	6,433	1,656
1965 1st qtr.	4,858	1,192	8,514	786	5,998	2,041	1,726	1,006	18,160	7,488	8,640	3,059	7,827	2,002

FIG. 27.   *Monthly Digest of Statistics.*   (By permission of the Controller of Her Majesty's Stationery Office.)

including installed plant, its capacity and type, can be found in *Electricity Undertakings of the World* (Benn, annual) which, unfortunately, ceased publication recently. Equipment exporters should also find useful a publication from the US Department of Commerce *Electric Current Abroad* (1959), which gives the type, phases, frequency, and voltages to be found in a large number of foreign cities.

Electrical Equipment

As for figures of exports and imports of electrical machinery, appliances, and other ancillary equipment, the main guides, covering 138 countries, are the United Nations *Yearbook of International Trade Statistics* and the *Monthly Bulletin of Statistics*. For Europe, in particular, there is the annual *Trade by Commodities* (2 vols.), published by OECD, and the quarterly *Foreign Trade* consisting of analytical abstracts showing the transactions of each member country with the main trading areas of the world.

Also published by the OECD are occasional monographs, including the *Survey of Electric Power Equipment*, 1962, and *Les Industries mécaniques et électriques: étude statistique*, 1961.

More exhaustive details can be found in specific government reports such as the monthly *Trade Overseas Accounts* and the *Annual Statement of the Trade of the UK* (HMSO). There is also the commercially published Garcke's *Statistical Record of British Electricity and Allied Manufacturing Industries*.

To help inquirers locate individual statistical publications are the following bibliographical guides: *Statistical Bulletins* (1954) and *Statistical Yearbooks* (1953) compiled by the United States Library of Congress, and the United Nations' *List of Statistical Series Collected by International Organizations* (1955). Extremely helpful because of its annual revision is the *Statesman's Yearbook* (Macmillan) which includes under each country a list of important official bulletins and gazettes.

Patents

Patents are rights granted by governments giving the patentee the sole right to make, use, or sell his invention during the period the patent remains in force. In return for this monopoly, the patentee reveals the details of his invention so that this record of technological progress is added to the sum of recorded knowledge and is available to the public at large.

The origins of the patent system are very ancient, and the Greeks, about 500 B.C., granted patents to cooks giving them exclusive rights for special dishes. British patent law reaches back to the twelfth century when the Crown granted charters and patents conferring monopolies on trade guilds, corporations, and sometimes individual persons. Under the Tudors and Stuarts there was much abuse of the patent system, and in 1601, in the House of Commons, Francis Bacon laid down the principle that monopoly should only be granted for a new manufacture. Parliament recognized this principle in 1624 and enacted the Statute of Monopolies which authorized letters patent and grants of privilege for the term of 14 years or under to the true and first inventor of the new manufactures and which others should not use.

This Section 6 of the Statute of Monopolies is still in force today (although the period of protection is now 16 years) and was the foundation of patent law throughout the world. The Patent Law Amendment Act of 1852 established the first Commissioners for Patents, and the Patent Office and the Register of Patents were set up. All new patents were printed and the 14,359 specifications from 1617 to 1852 were also printed and published together with indexes and a series of classified abridgements. *The Commissioners of Patents Journal* was started in the same year as the Act.

Various modifications and amendments followed until in 1949 the Patents Act consolidated old and new laws into one comprehensive piece of legislation. Further Acts were passed in 1957 and 1961.

An application for a patent may be made by the inventor himself, or by someone to whom he has assigned his rights, possibly his employer. The application must be accompanied by a specification, a document which is both technical and legal and for which a Patent Agent is usually employed as the compilation of a specification requires much skill and experience in drafting. The specification is given detailed examination in the Patent Office and this, together with subsequent necessary action may take up to about 2 years. A patent can only be granted for an invention which is a new manufacture or a new method or process of testing applicable to the improvement or control of manufacture. Although the examiner is concerned only with the novelty of the invention and, strictly, cannot challenge patentable merit, he is also to take notice of Section 10 of the Acts by which an application may be refused if it is "frivolous" because it claims as an invention something obviously contrary to well-established natural laws.

Besides people wishing to take out a patent who may wish to find out something about previous inventions in the field in which they are interested, many others may find patent specifications of considerable usefulness as they contain a great deal of technical information in some cases amounting to almost a state of the art survey. The specification consists of details of the full name, address, and nationality of the applicant and a title indicating the subject of the invention (often in very broad terms); a detailed description of the invention; and, finally, a statement of claim. The claims in effect define the monopoly which the patent will give and should define briefly and succinctly the tangible features of the invention for which protection is sought. Usually, the claims start off with one which is the broadest in scope followed by a number of others including additional features.

In order to facilitate searching, patents are classified according to the intrinsic nature of a process or apparatus rather than the immediate purpose for which it was designed. In 1963 the classification was radically altered and therefore a description of both the new and older classifications is necessary. Under the new scheme, the subject matter is classified under about 400 headings with altogether about 45,000 subdivisions, and these headings are grouped together for abridgement purposes. The abridgement groups of main concern to electrical engineering are:

F3 to 4   Armaments, lighting, heating, cooling, drying.
G1   Measuring.
G2 to 3   Optics, photography, regulating.
G4 to 6   Calculating, signalling, education, advertising, music, recording, nucleonics.
H1   Electric circuit elements.
H2   Electric power.
H3 to 5   Telecommunications, electronic circuits, electric heating.

Within these abridgement groups the headings are further detailed as in the following example:

H4   A   Aerials.
       D   Wave-energy position finding, etc.
       F   Television, copying telegraphy, etc.
       J   Audio transducers, local circuits, etc.
       K   Telephone exchanges, etc.
       L   Radio-frequency systems.
       P   Telegraphy.
       R   Line transmission systems.
       T   Cathode-ray tube circuits, etc.
       U   Inductive systems, etc.
       X   Sound magnifiers, etc.

In order to trace patents by subject, it is necessary to scan the published abridgements (Fig. 28) in the relevant classes. The Patent Office Library is the obvious source in London, but larger public libraries in other parts of the country have collections of British patents publications.

DIVISION H2

945,358. Electric motors. ASSOCIATED ELECTRICAL INDUSTRIES Ltd. June 2, 1961 [June 15, 1960], No. 21038/60. Heading H2A. [Also in Division F2]

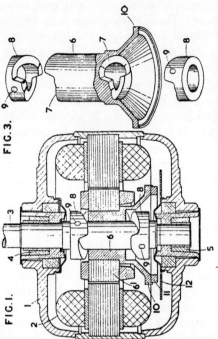

FIG. 1.

FIG. 3.

An electric motor has at each end of its rotor an axially facing annular cam each engaging a cam on the shaft so that limited axial movement of the rotor takes place when the rotor rotates relative to the stator. Fig. 1 shows an induction motor having a rotor support 6 rotatably mounted on its shaft. Cam surfaces 7 (Fig. 3) are formed at each end of the support and these engage cams 8 pinned to the shaft so that when over-run of the shaft occurs when the motor is switched off the rotor moves downwardly of the drawing. This brings a friction surface 11 mounted on the end 10 of the rotor support into contact with a stationary disc 12 to brake the rotary movement. A spring may be provided to urge the rotor in the direction which brings the friction surfaces into contact (Fig. 2, not shown). Specification 903,197 is referred to.

FIG. 28. *UK Patent Abridgments*, The Patent Office. (By permission of the Controller of Her Majesty's Stationery Office.)

If, however, a search must be made through specifications numbered before 940,000, different abridgement headings must be looked under. These groups, operative between 1931 and 1963, totalled 44 and were designated by Roman numerals.

The weekly *The Official Journal* (*Patents*) is the source for information about current complete specifications accepted and contains a list by serial number of applications to be made available for public inspection 6 weeks later. There are also indexes of application numbers, applicants' names, of subject matter, and there is a divisional allotment index which specifies the divisions in which abridgements are published. The *Official Journal* also contains information about proceedings taken under the Patents Act, 1949, and other official information.

US Patents

In the United States, the period of protection of patents is 17 years. *The Official Gazette of the United States Patent Office* (Fig. 29), weekly, not only lists current patents but provides an illustrated abstract for each one based usually on the first claim for each. These are arranged in classified order so that by consulting the *Manual of Classification* to discover relevant classification numbers it is possible to scan only those of interest in each issue of the *Official Gazette*. For retrospective searching (unless a visit is made to the Search Room of the United States Patent Office in Washington) it is necessary to consult lists of patents in each class and to consult these at a library holding a collection of complete specifications in numerical order. Since 1962 there has been published annually *The National Catalog of Patents*, a compilation of the year's patents in abridged form and arranged in classified order for the two subject areas of chemistry and electricity. This is issued by Rowman and Littlefield Inc., New York.

Guides to Patents

Some abstracting services provide information on patents. In particular *Chemical Abstracts* reviews new patents in its various

787

3,223,861
ELECTROMAGNETIC MOTOR
Rudolf Steiner, 17215 Valerio St., Van Nuys, Calif.
Filed Jan. 24, 1963, Ser. No. 253,692
1 Claim. (Cl. 310—21)

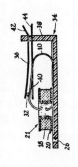

An electromagnetically actuated device comprising: a base having at least one mounting hole; a magnet coil having lugs mounted on said base; a single, continuous, magnetically conductive member having ends; said single, continuous, magnetically conductive member formed of resilient material to a shape so as to position said ends face to face with respect to each other across one single, operational air gap; said so formed single, continuous, magnetically conductive member being biased, by virtue of its inherent resilience, against a magnetizing force generated by said magnet coil, when energized, mounted on one portion of said base so as to position said single, operational air gap within the interior of said magnet coil, leaving its movable portion free to reciprocate toward and away from said mounted portion; a means for the control of electrical contacts mounted on the movable portion of said single, continuous, magnetically conduc-

controlling the relative magnitude of the voltages applied to said stators, two wound rotor units rotatable together and arranged to cooperate one with each of said stator units, and a rectifier bridge interconnecting said two rotor windings, whereby the highest E.M.F. from any phase winding of one rotor is always opposed to the highest E.M.F. generated in any phase winding of the second rotor.

3,223,863
ELECTRIC STARTING MECHANISM FOR
INTERNAL COMBUSTION ENGINES
Kenneth Preece and Roy Price Bowcott, Solihull, England, assignors to Joseph Lucas (Industries) Limited, Birmingham, England
Filed June 19, 1963, Ser. No. 289,112
Claims priority, application Great Britain, June 25, 1962,
24,269/62
3 Claims. (Cl. 310—75)

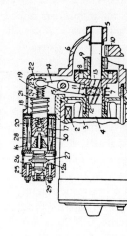

FIG. 29. *Official Gazette.* (By permission of the United States Patent Office, Washington, DC.)

K

fields of interest. About 5000 references a year are made to patents in a special section of the weekly *Electrical Review*, and a similar number appear in *Uniterm Electronics Patents Service*, Washington. *International Broadcast Engineer* each month carries brief abstracts of new British and American patents in its field of interest.

Some of the most comprehensive guides to world patents are provided by the Derwent Information Service, Theobalds Road, London, WC 1. These are in two categories: abstracts of patents by country such as *Soviet Inventions Illustrated – Section II: Electrical, Belgian Patents Report, French Patents Abstracts*, and *Japanese Patents Reports;* and guides on a subject basis such as *Fine Chemicals Patents Journal* and *Graphic Arts Patents Bulletin*. Another wide-ranging service is provided by *Interpas Monthly Patent Data Bulletins*, published in 26 sections and referring to patents of 20 countries. The same publishers, International Patents Service, POB 101, Den Bosch, Netherlands, issue *Japan Patent News*.

The Patent Office, London, provides a pamphlet free of charge on *Applying for a Patent* which gives fuller details of the patents system. Books which explain the subject include *Patent Protection: the inventor and his patent* by C. Lees (London, Business Publications, Ltd., 1965); *Patents and Registered Designs and their Exploitation* (Stevens, 1950) and *Patents for Inventions* (Stevens, 1955) both by T. A. Blanco White; *Ideas, Inventions and Patents* by R. A. Buckles (Wiley, 1957); and *Patent Law in the Research Laboratory* by J. K. Wise (Reinhold, 1955). The legal side for Britain is dealt with in *Terrell and Shelley on the Law of Patents* by K. E. Shelley (Sweet & Maxwell, 1961) and for the United States in *Patent Office Rules and Practice* by I. Seidman and Lester Horowitz (1962). International guides include *Patents* (*throughout the World* by W. W. White and B. G. Ravenscroft (Trade Activities, 1963) and the *Derwent Patents Manual* (both kept up to date).

Trade Marks

Trade marks are symbols readily identifying a particular brand of goods and may become an important factor in the sales appeal of the product. A trade mark is either a word, phrase, or device — or a combination of these. The Patent Office keeps a Register of Trade Marks and by means of which protection is given to registered marks. Before registration, however, a Trade Mark must be checked against the register to discover if a closely resembling, or even identical, trade mark has been previously registered for the same kind of goods. Goods are grouped into 34 classes and application must be made in respect of the appropriate class — or, if the trade mark covers goods in several classes, an application must be made for each class.

If the mark passes these first tests it must then be advertised in the *Trade Marks Journal* which is weekly and is, of course, published by the Patent Office. Any opposition to the registrations of the trade mark must be filed within a month. If there is no such opposition, or if any opposition is unsuccessful (as with patents, a case may get as far as the High Court), the trade mark is registered and remains in force for 7 years and can be renewed for further periods of 14 years each indefinitely.

There are restrictions on what can be accepted as a trade mark: for example it must consist of either the name of a company, individual, or firm represented in a special manner; the signature of the applicant (or his predecessor in the business); an invented word or words; or a word having no direct reference to the character or quality of the goods and not being a geographical name or surname. A device must be supported by evidence of its distinctiveness.

A pamphlet setting forth in more details the requirements can be obtained from the Patent Office. A useful concise introduction to the subject is *Practical Trade Mark Protection* by W. C. Duncan (Jordan & Sons Ltd., 1961).

Full information on trade marks of the world can be obtained from a loose-leaf manual kept up to date by a subscription supplement service: *Trade Marks throughout the World* by W. W. White and B. G. Ravenscroft (Trade Activities, Inc., New York), latest full edition 1963. More detailed information on changes in trade mark practice is found in *Patent and Trade Mark Review*. Various guides (mainly selective) to trade and brand names include *Brand Names for the Investor* by D. W. A. Gregg (London, Business Publications Ltd., 1963). For the English law of trade marks the standard work is *Kerly's Law of Trade Marks and Trade Names*, 9th edn., by T. A. B. White (Sweet & Maxwell, 1966). The comprehensive American work is *Trademark Law and Practice* by A. H. Seidel, S. Dubroff, and E. C. Gonda (Clark Boardman Co. Ltd., New York, 1963).

Trade Literature

Trade literature is produced by firms with the ultimate object of advertising their products to potential customers. It can take many forms, shapes, and sizes. Some of the most useful trade literature consists of periodicals, often called house journals, published by manufacturing firms and some of these are mentioned in the appropriate subject chapters. Catalogues and specifications form another important sector of trade literature and the technical librarian will build up as complete a collection of these as possible.

Most firms will make their trade literature freely available to all potential customers and even to others where it is felt that good use may be made of the material sent. Some firms, for example, Mullard Ltd., have also considerable education services to schools and technical colleges and supply teaching aids, films and film-strips and other non-book material as well as the more conventional pamphlets and books.

Much time may be spent in looking out for suitable trade literature and acquiring it even though once a person is on a mailing list theoretically new material should arrive at frequent intervals. Useful guides to availability are the features that appear regularly in technical and trade periodicals, although in many cases they tend to be selective.

Several commercial trade literature services are now available in Britain and America whereby for a subscription trade literature is sent, and in some cases filed and maintained, by the service organization. This obviates the chore of writing around to all the individual manufacturers, but as such services are not likely to be complete it may still be necessary for the librarian or engineer to search for further material.

An example of such a service in the United Kingdom is the *Electronic Engineering Index* which covers some 2000 different components and sub-assemblies (Technical Indexes Ltd., Index House, Ascot, Berkshire). With product data contributed by approximately 200 selected suppliers, some of whom manufacture in the United States, France, Italy, Germany, and Japan, the complete packaged unit is contained in 35 loose-leaf binders. Data sheets, catalogues, and brochures are arranged within a detailed classification scheme consisting of some 2000 different concepts. The search tool for the EEI library is the Product Index which allows location of a product either by function (using in conjunction a comprehensive subject index and classification schedules) or by company. Within the binders sub-groups of products are accompanied by indexing charts. These serve as guides not only to the specific literature of collaborating companies but also to other firms manufacturing products in that particular field.

EEI service staff call on every subscriber once every 4 weeks, putting in new catalogues, taking out obsolete material, and distributing copies of the monthly information *Bulletin*. Engineers, purchasing officers, and librarians should find the EEI a convenient and inexpensive method of handling an important but difficult type of information material.

In the United States there are several services of this kind, some making of use of microphotography techniques to save space as well as work and time. One service is known as "Vendor-Specs-Microfile" and offers manufacturers' specifications by industry group on microfilm. Catalogues of most of the firms represented in *Thomas' Register of American Manufacturers* are available in microform (4 by 6 in. microfiche) together with a portable reader designed by the Microcard Corporation. Another specialized service is provided by the *Directory of Technical Specifications— Electronic Test Instruments* (Technical Information Corporation, London Island).

Questions

1. What is the value of the patent system?

2. Why should an engineer consult patent specifications?

3. List large electrical firms that have submitted to the United Kingdom Patent Office within the past 3 months provisional specifications for acceptance.

4. What tables are of particular use to the electrical engineer?

5. Describe briefly the statistical sources you would use in the marketing and commercial department of a manufacturing company.

CHAPTER 10

History and Biography
UDC 621.3(09)

History

THERE is an abundance of resources, both primary and secondary, for the history of electrical engineering. A recent work which deals with the whole subject is *A History of Electrical Engineering* by Percy Dunsheath (Faber & Faber, 1962), a volume in the series Technology Today and Tomorrow. In 1955 the Science Museum, London, produced a *Classified List of Historical Events: mechanical and electrical engineering*, compiled by G. F. Westcott, which includes a bibliography. A series of papers on the history of electrical engineering by C. M. Jarvis was published in the *Journal of the Institution of Electrical Engineers* between 1955 and 1958 and later reprinted as a separate work.

Other recent works include *The Making of the Electronical Age: from the telegraph to automation* by H. I. Sharlin (1963) and *Men and Discoveries in Electricity* by B. Morgan (1952).

Histories of electricity and magnetism in the widest sense include Sir Edmund Whittaker's *A History of the Theories of Aether and Electricity*, 2 volumes, 1951–53; *Bibliographical History of Electricity and Magnetism* by P. F. Mottelay, 1922; and the National Electrical Manufacturers' Association's (of the United States) *A Chronological History of Electrical Development from 600 B.C.* (1966).

The growth of the electrical industry is traced in an American work *The Rise of the Electrical Industry during the 19th Century* by M. MacLaren (1943), and R. H. Parsons has written on *Early Days of the Power Station Industry* (1939).

The Development of Electrical Technology in the 19th Century by W. James King is in 3 parts, and these form Papers 28, 29, and 30 of *Contributions from the Museum of History and Technology* of the US National Museum, Bulletin 228. They were published as well-illustrated separate pamphlets in 1962.

The story of electrical engineering is at first that of the pioneering efforts of individuals, then later it is the work of groups — firms and associations — that becomes more prominent. Biographies are dealt with later in this chapter, but there are several histories of institutions. *The History of the Institution of Electrical Engineers, 1871–1931* by R. Appleyard was published in 1939 by the Institution; Chapter XIX of Dunsheath (see above) is also relevant. The history of the Institute of Radio Engineers was detailed in the *Proceedings of the IRE*, **45** (5), 597–635 (May 1957) (by L. E. Whittemore), and the story of the American Institute of Physics appeared in *Physics Today*, **(9)** (1), 56–58, 60, 62, 64, 66, in a paper by H. A. Barton. The October 1956 issue of the *Post Office Electrical Engineers' Journal* (**49**, Part 3) contained altogether 15 papers on the history and activities of the Institution of Post Office Electrical Engineers to commemorate its 50th anniversary.

Most branches of electrical engineering have their historical surveys. Lighting is dealt with in *A History of Luminescence from the Earliest Times until 1944* by N. Harvey (American Philosophical Society, 1957). A slimmer work is W. T. O'Dea's *Short History of Lighting* (HMSO, 1959). The same author also wrote *The Social History of Lighting* (1958).

The History of Electric Wiring is by J. Mellanby (1957) and deals with the development of wiring from 1870 to the present. Electric traction forms an important part of the history of underground railways, and there is a comprehensive account by A. A. Jackson and D. F. Croome, *Rails Through the Clay: a history of London's tube railways* (1962).

A recent study is *Early Electrical Communication*, by E. A. Marland (1964).

A very detailed work on early electric telegraphy is *A History of Electric Telegraphy to the year 1837* by J. J. Fahie: it was published in 1884 and has a bibliography of some 200 items. Fahie also wrote *A History of Wireless Telegraphy 1838–1889* (1890).

T. Wilson contributed a paper to a symposium published in 1958, *The Structure of British Industry*, edited by D. Burns, on the economic and technical development of the British electronics industry from 1896 (pp. 130–83 of vol. 2 of the symposium). There are many works on the history on radio communication. G. L. Archer covered *The History of Radio to 1926* (American Historical Society, 1938) and G. G. Blake wrote *History of Radio Telegraphy and Telephony* (1926), a work which contains a very extensive bibliography. More recent developments are dealt with in *Inventions and Innovations in the Radio Industry* by W. R. MacLaurin (1949).

The Development of Power Cables was described by Hunter and Hazell (1956). *History of the Telephone in the United Kingdom* by F. G. C. Baldwin (1925) is a useful work, and the Institution of Electrical Engineers published in 1955 a history of *Thermionic Valves, 1904–1954: the first fifty years.*

From time to time manufacturing firms publish works in connection with their own historical development. Sometimes these take the form of a more general history such as *The Evolution of Electro-magnetic Machines* by E. Kuffel (1961), commissioned by Pinchin Johnson & Co. An American publication of this sort is *The Fuse: its story*, written by R. Griffith, 1943, for the Chase-Shawmut Company. A number of straightforward histories of firms have been produced. Examples are *The Telcon Story* (1950) (the Telegraph Construction and Maintenance Co.), *History of the House of Siemens* by G. Siemens (1957), and R. E. Crompton's *Reminiscences* (1928).

The setting of the electrical industry and its branches in the wider social, economic, and political context may be studied in such works as S. G. Sturmey's *The Economic Development of Radio* (1958) and Asa Briggs's definitive *History of Broadcasting in the United Kingdom* (in progress, vol. 1 published in 1961; vol. 2 in 1965).

There are many histories of science and technology and two useful guides to the literature are George Sarton's *Horus: a guide to the history of science* (1952), which deals with societies, institutes, congresses, museums, etc.; types of printed material including periodicals, encyclopedias, and atlases; abstracting and reviewing journals; and with science by country and by subject. *Scientific Books, Libraries and Collectors*, 2nd edn., 1962, by J. L. Thornton and R. I. J. Tulley (The Library Association) comments mainly on books that have made an important contribution to the development of science. It contains a bibliography, in alphabetical order of author, occupying pp. 318–73.

The late Professor Sarton's own *Introduction to the History of Science* (5 vols., 1927–48), although covering only the early periods, is an important work, while H. T. Pledge's *Science since 1500* (1939) is a short history of mathematics, physics, chemistry, and biology. Two works by A. Wolf are *A History of Science, Technology and Philosophy in the Sixteenth and Seventeenth Centuries* (1950) and *A History of Science and Technology in the Eighteenth Century*, 2nd edn., 1952.

A symposium, *A Century of Technology*, ed. by P. Dunsheath, 1951, covers the period 1851–1951 and includes a contribution on electrical engineering. The standard work on the development of technology is the impressive *A History of Technology*, published by the Clarendon Press and edited by Charles Singer and others in 5 volumes, 1954–8. Each chapter is by a specialist and is liberally supplied with bibliographies, illustrations, plans, tables, etc. Singer is also the author of some smaller works including *A Short History of Scientific Ideas to 1900* (1959), considered to be the best of the shorter histories.

The widespread, and still growing, interest in the history of science is seen by the appointment to British universities since 1945 of Readers or Lecturers in the subject; by international activities such as the 11th International Congress on the History of Science held at Warsaw in August 1965 at which a large exhibition of books and periodicals dealing with the subject was held; and by the many scholarly periodicals published in various countries.

In Britain are published, among others, *Annals of Science*, a quarterly review of the history of science and technology since the Renaissance; *British Journal for the History of Science*, published twice yearly by the British Society for the History of Science; *History of Science*, an annual review of literature, research, and teaching; *Journal of Industrial Archaeology* (quarterly) published by the Newcomen Society for the Study of the History of Engineering and Technology whose *Transactions* are another important source. Two international journals, both formerly edited by Sarton, are *Isis* (quarterly) and *Osiris* which specializes in longer and more technical studies than *Isis*. From the United States there is the *Chronicle of the Early American Industries Association Inc.*

Lychnos; Lärdomshistoriska Samfundets Årsbok, published annually in Uppsala, Sweden, since 1936, reviews between 150 and 200 books relating to the history of science.

Physis; Rivista de Storia della Scienza is published quarterly in Florence, Italy, and has a book review section and a further list of publications received.

A full and comprehensive bibliography of writings in English on the historical development of electrical engineering and electrophysics was published in *The Bulletin of Bibliography*, vol. 20, nos. 3–7, December 1950 to January–April 1952. This was compiled by Thomas J. Higgins and copies of the collected off-print (26 pages) may be found in some libraries.

Other useful bibliographies on the history of electrical engineering include pp. 5–8 of Moore and Spencer's *Electronics: a bibliographical guide* (1961), the British Council's booklist *Recent British Books on the History of Science*, *A Bibliography of Electricity and Magnetism 1860–1883* by G. May (1884), and

The Early History of Science: a short handlist, published for the Historical Association in 1950.

Isis has a section which is a critical bibliography of the history of science and its cultural influences and contains about 2000 references annually to world literature. There is a subject and chronological arrangement.

Archives Internationales d'Histoire des Sciences contains, quarterly, about 200 abstracts a year from international sources, while Section 22 of *Bulletin Signalétique* is concerned with the history of science and technology. There are annual subject and author indexes to its 3000 entries. A Belgian source is *Notes Bibliographiques Relative à l'Histoire des Sciences*, which has been published semi-annually since 1946.

Biography

Information may be required about the lives and works of individuals, living or dead, and there are many potential sources of information.

Scientists of the past, particularly the greater ones, may have at least brief entries in general encyclopedias such as the *Encyclopedia Britannica, Chambers's Encyclopedia, Colliers Encyclopedia*, etc. Fuller information will be found, however, in various biographical dictionaries, national and international.

The Dictionary of National Biography (29 vols.), published first in parts between 1885 and 1900, is the largest of national biographical dictionaries and with its various supplements covers British notabilities from the earliest times up to 1950. A concise edition in 2 volumes has also been published. Corrections and additions resulting from recent research are published in the *Bulletin of the Institute of Historical Research. Who Was Who 1897–1960* (in 5 vols.) contains entries removed from *Who's Who* (see later) because of the death of the biographee during the period under treatment. Two guides to biographical material are by W. Matthews: *British Autobiographies* (1955) and *British Diaries* (1950), and each lists British autobiographies or diaries published or written before 1951 and 1942 respectively.

Other national biographical dictionaries of importance include the *Dictionary of American Biography* (giving biographies up to the date of death 1940), the *Allgemeine Deutsche Biographie* (56 vols., biographies up to 1899), *Dictionnaire de Biographie Française* (in progress), and *Dizionario Biografica degli Italiano* (also in progress).

Several important works deal with scientific biography. J. C. Poggendorff's *Biographisch-literatisches Handwörterbuch* covers the lives and writings of scientists on an international basis. The first 2 volumes deal with scientists to 1857 and subsequent volumes cover specified periods. Living scientists appear in the current volumes. Two works published by the Royal Society are of great value: *Obituary Notices of Fellows of the Royal Society, 1932–1954* and *Biographical Memoirs of Fellows of the Royal Society* (1955 onwards) give long accounts of the life, work, and writings of deceased fellows. Before 1932, these biographies were published in the Society's *Proceedings*.

Briefer details on the major scientists of all countries can be found in *Chambers's Dictionary of Scientists* (1951), while works such as J. G. Crowther's *British Scientists of the Nineteenth Century* (1935) may be useful. Individual biographies include *Michael Faraday: a biography* (1965) by L. Pearce Williams, and the shorter *Michael Faraday: father of electricity* (1962) by David Gunston, *The Life of James Clerk Maxwell* by L. Campbell and W. Garnett (1882), *Edison* by M. Josephson (1959), *The Inventor of the Valve* by J. T. MacGregor Morris (1954), and many others.

Information on contempories will be found in *Who's Who* (annual) (entries compiled from a questionnaire sent to each biographee), *Who's Who in America*, *Wer is Wer?*, *Chi è?*, and other similar sources. *The International Who's Who* and *Who's Who in International Organizations* give wide coverage.

The *Directory of British Scientists*, in its 3rd edition, 1966, will give details of over 50,000 science graduates of British universities, and it will include 52 lists classifying them according to their branches of scientific interest.

American Men of Science: a biographical directory is a standard reference work first published in 1960 which has now reached its 10th edition in 5 volumes (four concerned with the physical and biological sciences and one with the social and behavioral sciences). There are about 96,000 names in these 4 volumes and each entry gives information about the biographee's career, present post, and particular subject interests. There is, however, no information about published works.

For information about Russian scientists and engineers, *Soviet Men of Science* by John Turkevich (1963) is a collection of brief biographies about more than 400 prominent Soviet physical and biological scientists. Major interests and achievements of each are given together with further biographical references and a bibliography of writings for each scientist.

The fullest source for information on British electrical engineers is *Electrical Who's Who* (annual) published by Iliffe Books for the Electrical Review. As well as biographies it includes lists of the staffs of firms and organizations such as the Electricity Council, Central Electricity Generating Board, etc.

Another and constantly up-to-date source consists of brief biographies given by many periodicals concerning their contributors and, even when these are not present, the writer's present post and company or organization usually appears at the head of the article.

The annual *Constitution and List of Members* of the Institution of Electronic and Radio Engineers (formerly, until 26 February 1964, the British Institution of Radio Engineers) gives names and addresses of members in the various grades such as member, associate member, graduates, etc., together with dates of the original status of the member and year of election. It also gives a topographical list of members including those in overseas countries and details of the membership of the Institution's various committees as well as representation on other bodies including British Standards Institution Committees. A similar type of publication, the *ECA Year Book* of the Electrical Contractors Association (Inc.), gives its main membership list under geographical branch headings with an alphabetical list as an index to it.

Questions

1. Outline the growth of the electronics industry in the United Kingdom. List the relevant literature you have used.

2. Where would you find material on the life and work of Michael Faraday?

3. Is the study of the history of electrical engineering of any practical use to the engineer?

CHAPTER II

Power Generation and Supply
UDC 621.311 to 621.316

Bibliographies

GUIDES for the selection of books and other material relevant to
this chapter and the ones that follow have already been covered
in Chapters 2 and 3. The catalogues of the special libraries in the
field are of importance in this respect particularly those compiled
by the CEGB and the Electrical Research Association, Leatherhead. The latter issued a catalogue of books and periodicals in
December 1956, part 1 of which was a subject arrangement
according to the UDC. The second part, which listed the periodicals received in the library, was revised and issued as a separate
in 1964. This list of holdings covers more than 500 titles. Also
highly relevant is the third supplement of the Lending Library
Catalogue published by the Institution of Electrical Engineers
covering the period January 1959 to June 1964. Useful, too, is
the 1965 revision of the catalogue of books on Electrical and
Electronic Engineering, available from the H. K. Lewis's Lending
Library.

Handbooks, Treatises and Textbooks

A standard work covering British practice in power station
operation is T. H. Carr's *Electric Power Stations*, in 2 volumes
and published by Chapman & Hall. Published first in 1941 it
has reached a 4th edition (1955–6; reprint 1961–2). The whole
field is covered from the fundamentals of design to hydroelectric,

diesel, electric, and gas turbine plant. Bibliographies are included with each chapter.

Very useful for students of electricity supply is the published version of a correspondence tuition course introduced by the Central Electricity Generating Board, *Modern Power Station Practice*, 5 volumes, 1963. The compilers have attempted to cover all possible fields of future developments, including nuclear power generation (vol. 5). Each volume has a bibliography. A practical treatise for those engaged in the supply of electrical energy, and in its 6th edition (first published 1923), is J. W. Meares' *Electrical Engineering Practice*, Chapman & Hall, 1958.

The remarkable increase in hydroelectric power production since the war has inspired several good technical books covering United States practice. A reputable treatise for modern developments in Great Britain, the Commonwealth countries, and Europe, is the 3-volume work *Hydro-Electric Engineering Practice*, edited by J. Guthrie Brown, with contributions from a number of specialists (Blackie, 1958). Volume 1, covering civil engineering aspects, reached a 3rd edition in 1964; vol. 2 deals with mechanical and electrical engineering; and vol. 3 economics, operation and maintenance.

Transmission Lines

The trend towards the transmission of higher-power voltages has thrown emphasis on the design, construction, and performance of lines and cables. A really basic book dealing with first principles is Edwin B. Kurz's *The Lineman's Handbook* (McGraw-Hill). First published in 1928 and now in a 4th edition (1964) it describes in detail all steps necessary in locating, erecting, testing, inspecting, and maintaining electrical distribution and transmission lines. A general introduction written for the engineer is G. C. Gracey's *Overhead Electric Power Lines* (Benn, 1963). A more advanced review of basic design and engineering data is C. C. Barnes' *Power Cables: design and installation*, 2nd edn. (Chapman & Hall, 1966).

Transformers

There are a number of good books on this subject both for the designer and the student. A non-mathematical approach is one of the Westinghouse–McGraw-Hill series *Transformer Principles and Practice* by J. B. Gibbs, 2nd edn., 1950. In the same series is *Transformers for the Electric Power Industry* by R. L. Bean and others, 1959. Another example of industrial participation is *Transformer Engineering* by L. F. Blume and others, 2nd edn., published by Wiley for the General Electric in the Advancement of Engineering Practice series.

Voltage Control

Other important aspects of electric power distribution include rectifiers, amplifiers, relays, and switchgear, but the representative literature is too voluminous to mention here. A field of increasing importance to the electrical and electronic engineer is the maintenance of constant or near-constant voltage (see G. K. Moore and K. J. Spencer's *Electronics: a bibliographical guide*). A recent publication suitable for students and others is G. N. Patchett's *Automatic Voltage Regulators and Stabilizers* (Pitman), now in its 2nd edn. (1964). For research workers wishing to continue their reading in this currently extensive field, the author has provided a bibliography of 1300 references. Another book with an extensive bibliography is F. A. Benson's *Voltage Stabilized Supplies* (Macdonald, 1957).

Direct Conversion

A new area of electric power generation that is attracting considerable interest is that of the direct conversion of energy. Keeping abreast with the rapid developments in such a field can only be done effectively by following the various symposia that are held from time to time. For example, the one sponsored by the Institution of Electrical engineers *Magnetoplasmadynamic Electric Power Generation* was published in 1962. Other have been held in the United States and in Britain. Pergamon Press, for example, published the proceedings of a colloquium organized at Sheffield University in 1961 under the title of *Advances in Magnetohydrodynamics*. A useful book that has consolidated much of the current thought on the subject is R. A. Coombes's *Magnetohydrodynamic Generation of Electric Power* (Chapman & Hall, 1964) based on lectures given by various recognized authorities at the Salford College of Advanced Technology. A good bibliography is included.

Organizations

Outstanding for its worldwide scope and the study of fossil energy sources is the World Power Conference, a standing body with national committees, formed in 1924 as a link between the different branches of power and fuel technology; between the experts of the different countries throughout the world; and between engineers and others closely concerned. It deals with all forms of energy including nuclear, particularly with reference to their inter-relationship. The conference has consultative status with the Economic and Social Council of United Nations and co-operates with the International Atomic Energy Agency and the World Meteorological Organization. It is a member of the Union of International Engineering Organizations.

Plenary conferences are held every 6 years. The 6th conference took place at Melbourne in 1962 when the theme was *The Changing Pattern of Power*, represented by over 200 papers. The *Transactions* were published in 14 volumes, with papers in English or French. More frequent sectional meetings are devoted to limited aspects, for example, in 1960 (Madrid) — Solving power shortage problems: 1964 (Lausanne) — Losses in the field of energy economics. (Reference: *Electricity*, November–December 1964, pp. 333–5). Other aspects of power generation on an international basis are divided between four other organizations: the International Union of Producers and Distributors of Electrical Energy (UNIPEDE), the International Commission on Large Dams (ICOLD), the International Conference of Large Electrical

Systems (CIGRÉ), and the Union for the Co-ordination of the Production and Transport of Electrical Power (UCPTE).

UNIPEDE, specifically concerned with production transmission and distribution has separate committees for the study of nuclear energy, thermal generation, hydroelectric generation, international interconnections, distribution tariffs, development of the applications of electrical energy, and statistics. An international congress is held every 3 years; thirteen have taken place since its formation in 1925. The 1964 conference held in Scandinavia resulted in 2 volumes of *Compte Rendu*. The regular Bulletin *L'Economie Electrique*, published quarterly, includes annually a special international statistical issue.

ICOLD, which was sponsored in 1928 by the World Power Conference, also holds international congresses every 3 years covering such aspects of dam construction as concrete, underground works, measurement and apparatus, hydrology, and silting. It publishes transactions, a bulletin, a technical dictionary, and a *World Register of Dams*.

CIGRÉ, founded in 1921, covers the generation of electrical energy (excluding the prime mover) and transmission up to and including the low-voltage side of the transmission transformer. Meetings are held every 2 years and the papers read (approximately 120) are published as *Proceedings* in 3 volumes. A regular publication *Electra*, available only to members, appears three times a year.

The members of UCPTE, executives and experts of large European electrical power companies, have as their aims research on the most effective utilization of existing or potential means of the production and transport of electrical power, particularly by international exchange. Working groups study specific technical problems and their reports are communicated through the *Rapport annuel*. A quarterly *Bulletin trimestriel* contains forecasts on the supply of electrical power, a survey of the power situation and exchanges between neighbouring countries, etc.

Utilities

Apart from routine generation and supply, the major producers of electrical power throughout the world are heavily involved in research and development. Much of their work is naturally confidential and the report literature that evolves is unobtainable, at least by those not directly concerned with the industry. The scientific and technological personnel involved communicate more freely, however, both at national and international meetings and through the medium of society and institutional journals.

Great Britain

The largest electricity supply system in the world under unified operational control is that administered by the Central Electricity Generating Board. Responsible for the operation of power stations and the main transmission network, the Board sells electricity in bulk to the twelve Area Electricity Boards responsible for distribution to consumers. Because of its large and important commitments any publication from the CEGB, and from the Electricity Council — the co-ordinating and planning body for the electricity supply industry, can be regarded as significant. Annual statistical and progress reports can be obtained through HMSO; technical and utilization research reports freely available are notified in CEGB's Information Department's monthly abstracts bulletin (see below) or in the bi-monthly journal *Electricity*, published by the Electricity Council. This journal reports on the activities of the CEGB, Area Boards, and foreign undertakings, and covers important conferences. A number of papers outlining research activities were included in the Proceedings of two Conferences of University Professors in 1958 and 1961, organized by the Electricity Council.

For the electrical industry in general the focal point for information in the United Kingdom is the British Electrical and Allied Manufacturers' Association (BEAMA). The Association maintains an economic and statistical service and produces technical and commercial publications and economic surveys

Destinations and Values of British Electrical and Allied Exports 1962-64—(continued)

THE COMMONWEALTH

Value in £000's

	ELECTRIC MOTORS											
	Not Exceeding One-Third h.p.			Exceeding One-Third but under 1 h.p.			1—250 h.p.			Exceeding 250 h.p.		
Destination	1962	1963	1964	1962	1963	1964	1962	1963	1964	1962	1963	1964
Gibraltar	1·2	·2	·2	·1	·1	—	·8	1·6	2·7	—	—	—
Malta and Gozo	1·5	·6	·5	1·5	·5	1·8	4·9	2·7	8·3	—	—	—
Cyprus	·7	2·7	2·4	1·8	1·6	2·2	14·0	24·2	11·9	1·0	—	1·4
Gambia	·1	—	—	—	—	—	—	·6	—	—	—	—
Sierra Leone	·2	·3	·5	—	·2	·2	·1	—	·1	—	—	—
Ghana	2·1	1·4	1·3	1·9	5·1	2·3	6·9	7·0	14·2	—	—	15·9
Nigeria	1·6	4·1	2·6	2·1	3·6	4·2	19·1	22·9	25·5	3·3	7·9	1·5
Rhodesia—Nyasaland	6·8	6·4	8·3	17·6	9·1	14·9	50·8	56·9	97·1	38·8	23·7	33·4
Tanganyika	1·4	·7	—	·4	—	·3	115·1	95·0	98·3	35·7	150·2	54·2
Zanzibar	—	·1	—	—	—	·1	·6	12·8	21·9	4·0	—	1·1
Kenya	1·2	3·4	3·1	1·3	3·8	3·1	34·4	58·2	63·7	—	—	—
Uganda	—	·2	·1	—	—	·1	2·4	4·6	11·3	—	—	—
Bahrain	1·1	1·3	1·0	·5	·8	·5	4·4	6·3	5·3	—	—	2·3
India	24·3	20·1	13·1	7·3	6·9	13·0	367·1	477·6	255·3	93·4	158·1	139·4
Pakistan	3·3	2·1	13·3	14·0	17·3	9·8	286·0	150·6	174·3	10·9	8·4	10·5
Malaysia	11·8	16·8	17·6	10·5	12·2	17·2	149·7	153·7	159·1	33·6	13·9	50·8
Ceylon	4·5	2·9	3·0	2·8	3·3	6·0	56·1	67·3	53·8	—	8·2	—
Hong Kong	18·9	33·6	45·3	23·9	43·0	45·4	146·5	179·5	267·1	14·4	59·9	24·1
Australia	103·9	110·7	127·7	25·0	67·0	53·1	1,071·3	948·5	1,355·5	805·2	417·2	633·6

Fig. 30. *Territorial Analysis of UK Exports and Imports.* (By permission of the British and Allied Manufacturers' Association.)

relating to the electrical industry. Publications include *The BEAMA Directory* and an annual *Territorial Analysis of UK Exports and Imports of Electrical and Allied Machinery and Apparatus* (Fig. 30). BEAMA works closely with the National Economic Development Office in the preparation of surveys and reports dealing with major sectors of the electrical manufacturing industry and studies cover rates of growth in output, capacity, employment, and exports.

France

Whilst it has not the same monopoly, Electricité de France supplies three-quarters of the French population and is also making a significant effort in research and development. Its main publication is the annual *Rapport d'Activite Comptes de Gestion* and its more popular illustrated presentation *Travaux d'Investissement*. Some technical reports are made available and Press releases are regularly sent out.

Other European Countries

Germany, Belgium and the Netherlands do not have national-ized undertakings, and electric power production is in the hands of private, municipal, or industrial producers. Italy, however, nationalized its electricity industry in 1963, operating under the National Electricity Board.

United States of America

The US power pattern is also one of a large number of utilities — private, federal, municipal, and co-operative. The large producers such as the Tennessee Valley Authority, California Electric, Consolidated Edison, Illinois Power, Pacific Power and Light, Philadelphia Electric, and so on, disseminate technical information from time to time through various media. There is a government co-ordinating body, however, the Federal Power Commission, which publishes information on the electric power industry generally, studies plans for proposed hydro schemes, and participates with other government agencies in co-ordinating efforts towards the development and utilization of water and related land resources. Apart from regular annual reports, the Commission has published recently a very significant *National Power Survey* that sets out guide lines for developing the US electricity supply industry.

Important as an information source is the Edison Electric Institute, New York, formed in 1933 as a trade association with membership open to electrical power operating companies and electric utility holding companies. It serves as both a forum for the discussion and exchange of information on industrial problems and a sponsor for co-operative research. Its work is conducted through 80 standing committees who investigate and report on new developments. The Institute distributes a large number of publications, all dealing with the electrical power industry. Regularly published are the monthly *EEI Bulletin*, monthly statistical compilations *Data of Interest*, the bi-monthly *Farm Electrification Magazine*, and weekly, monthly, and annual statistical reports. It also issues committee reports and publicity literature, plays an important part in developing codes and standards, and distributes material prepared by individuals, power companies, and manufacturers.

Japan

This is another highly industrialized country with a number of different power companies, but each has a state-granted monopoly for a particular region. Government supervision is effected through the Public Utilities Bureau and the Ministry of International Trade and Industry. Responsibility for the collection and analysis of relevant data lies with the Overseas Electrical Industry Survey Institute which issues an annual progress report *The Electric Power Industry in Japan*.

Technological activities and research and development in Japan are reported by the Association for International Co-operation in Tokyo. Another useful source of information is the government-supported Japan Electric Power Survey Committee which publishes every 6 months *Electric Power Survey*.

Periodicals

Useful for power supply statistics is the Electricity Council's *Electricity*, already discussed above. Another useful periodical is the official journal of the Electrical Power Engineers' Association, *Electrical Power Engineer*, which is published monthly and carries Association news. A good representative house journal is *Electrical Distribution*, concerned with the products and activities of the Cable and Construction Divisions of Associated Electrical Industries Ltd. A long-established Australian journal concerned with power generation, electricity transmission, and utilization, is *Electrical Engineer*, published monthly by the Tait Publishing Co. in Melbourne. United States activities are covered by *Public Power*, the monthly journal of the American Public Power Association, while *Public Utilities Fortnightly* is concerned more with the business and administrative side.

Abstracts

An important source of abstracts for power generation and supply and for electrical engineering generally is the Central Electricity Generating Board's *Digest* which has been published fortnightly since 1949. It contains some 2000 abstracts per year from journal, report, and conference literature on an international basis, arranged by a subject classification. There are annual subject and author indexes.

Energy Review (monthly), published by the Technical Publishing Co., Barrington, Illinois, contains about 2400 summaries and 200 abstracts per year from English-language literature. *Direct Energy Conversion Literature Abstracts*, a publication of the US Naval Research Laboratory, was formerly known as *Thermoelectricity Abstracts* and covers energy storage, regulation, and control. It is published irregularly but, on average, contains about 1500 abstracts per year from world literature.

For information on Russian progress and development in power generation and supply, *Power Express* should be consulted. This is one of the series published by International Physical

Index Inc., of New York, and in its 12 issues each year it prints some 500 complete papers, excerpts, and abstracts a year from 98 Russian technical journals. The journal *Power* has a section, "Technical Briefs", containing between 200 and 250 abstracts each year.

In German, the *Technisches Zentralblatt. Abteilung Energiewesen* covers world literature on physics and energy.

The appropriate section of *Referativnyi Zhurnal: Silovye Ustanovski* contains nearly 15,000 abstracts a year from world literature, while the Russian journal *Energetik* carries about 100 abstracts a year from Russian literature. The Hungarian *Müszaki Lapszemle. Energia* abstracts non-Hungarian literature including patents and gives UDC numbers.

CHAPTER 12

Measurements and Instrumentation
UDC 621.317

THIS field is well covered by good text and reference books, although several of the standard works are somewhat dated. *Electrical Measuring Instruments* by C. V. Drysdale and A. C. Jolley (London, Chapman & Hall) reached a 2nd edition in 1952 and at the time provided information on nearly every important type of instrument. Another comprehensive treatment for the student and practising engineer, and planned as a companion volume to Terman's *Radio Engineering*, is *Electronic Measurements* by F. E. Terman and J. M. Pettit, 2nd edn., 1952 (New York, McGraw-Hill).

A more recent survey covering a wide range of instruments for very high and very low values, for remote indication, and for increased accuracy, is E. H. W. Banner's *Electronic Measuring Instruments*, 2nd edn., 1958 (London, Chapman & Hall). Provided with good bibliographies and illustrations is *Electrical Measurements and Measuring Instruments* by E. W. Golding and F. C. Widdis (London, Pitman, 1963) which has run through 5 editions since it was first published in 1933. Other useful books include F. K. Harris, *Electrical Measurements* (New York, Wiley, 1952), restricted to direct-current and low frequency measurement; J. D. Craggs, and J. M. Meek, *High-voltage Laboratory Techniques* (London, Butterworth, 1954); I. F. Kinnard, *Applied Electrical Measurements* (Wiley, 1956), one of the General Electric series for the Advancement of Engineering Practice and supplied with liberal bibliographies for more thorough studies; W. C. Michels, *Electrical Instruments and their Applications* (New York, Van Nostrand, 1957); G. R. Partridge, *Principles of Electronic Instruments* (NJ, Prentice-Hall, 1958).

In the more specialized field of microwave techniques an essential reference work is the *Handbook of Microwave Measurements*, 3rd edn. by M. Sucher and J. Fox, in 3 volumes. Published in 1963 by the Microwave Research Institute at the Polytechnic Institute of Brooklyn and distributed by Interscience, it puts emphasis on the need for a deeper insight and better understanding of the quantities to be measured and their relationship to basic or derived parameters. The Polytechnic Institute of Brooklyn has also published a *Handbook of Electronic Measurements*, edited by M. Wind, in 2 volumes, 1956, and various Proceedings of MRI Symposia.

Very much dated but still important for some of its basic information is C. G. Montgomery's *Technique of Microwave Measurements* (McGraw-Hill, 1947), published in the highly reputable MIT Radiation Laboratory series. Another useful reference book from the same publisher dealing with fundamental methods and more special applications is *Microwave Measurements* by E. L. Ginzton (1957).

One of the most versatile devices designed for analysis of all kinds, and wherever electronic equipment is used, is the cathode-ray oscilloscope. The basic reference book for this field of application is the *Encyclopedia of Cathode-ray Oscilloscopes and their Uses*, compiled by J. F. Rider and S. D. Uslan, 2nd edn., 1959 (New York, J. F. Rider; London, Chapman & Hall). Other useful books are J. H. Reyner's *Cathode-ray Oscillographs*, 5th edn. (Pitman, 1957), an introduction to principles and practice; and I. A. D. Lewis and F. H. Wells's *Millimicrosecond Pulse Techniques*, 2nd edn. (Pergamon, 1959).

Organizations

Very important for the development of the science and technology of measurement and its application in research and industry is the British Scientific Instrument Research Association

(SIRA), at Chislehurst, Kent. Its membership includes both the makers and users of instruments, and so constitutes a vital link between these two major interests. A comprehensive library and technical inquiry services are provided for members. "Where-to-buy" inquiries are answered with the support of a well-indexed collection of trade literature.

Much of the technical literature produced by the Association relates to work carried out in its laboratories and is therefore confidential to members. More generally available, however, are: *Instrument Abstracts* (see below); *Instrument Construction*, an English-language edition of the Russian monthly journal *Priborostroenie*; the textbook *A Guide to Instrument Design*; and a number of monographs that are chiefly surveys of accessible information on particular topics. Recently a technical and advisory service on measurement and control technology (SIRAID) has been made available. This service can be used by anyone who has a problem connected with the applications of instrumentation and control (see SIRA, *Impact*, No. 4, obtainable from the Head of Information Group, SIRA, South Hill, Chislehurst, Kent).

Two other organizations of significance are the National Physical Laboratory, Teddington, which publishes reports and monographs on instrumentation and occasional symposia, and the Physical Society. A very important annual event organized by the latter is the Physical Society Exhibition which includes new and prototype equipment not previously seen publicly.

Periodicals

The authoritative *Journal of Scientific Instruments*, published monthly by the Institute of Physics and the Physical Society, is one of the major British periodicals dealing with instrumentation. Also of importance are *Transactions of the Society of Instrument Technology* published quarterly. Useful commercial publications are *Instrument Practice*, a United Trade Press publication (monthly), which additionally covers the wider field of control systems, electronics, and automation and *Instrument Review*, published monthly by Morgan Brothers. Two Commonwealth journals are the *Australian Journal of Instrument Technology*, the official journal of the Australian Society of Instrument Technology, and *Canadian Controls and Instrumentation*, a Maclean-Hunter monthly publication which contains current patent information.

The Instrument Society of America publishes two important periodicals — the monthly *ISA Journal* and the quarterly *ISA Transactions*. The US National Bureau of Standards publishes its *Journal of Research* in several sections of which Section C, Engineering and Instrumentation (quarterly), contains many advanced papers. The American Institute of Physics is responsible for the *Review of Scientific Instruments* published monthly since 1930. *Instruments and Control Systems* is a large circulation monthly journal published by the Instruments Publishing Co. and it includes a special section on simulators. Very important for research workers is *IEEE Transactions on Instrumentation and Measurement*, one of the many fields covered by the Institute's specialized groups.

Three Russian journals are available in English translation: *Instrument Construction* (originally *Priborostroenie*, mentioned earlier); *Instruments and Experimental Techniques* (*Pribory i Tekhnika Eksperimenta*, produced by the Instrument Society of America); and *Measurement Techniques* (*Izmeritel'naia Tekhnika*, also ISA). East European journals (not translated) include *Meres es Automatika* issued by the Scientific Association of Measuring Technique and Automation, Budapest (with summaries in English, German, and Russian), and *Pomiary, Automatyka, Kontrola* issued by the Polish Committee on Measuring and Automation.

Among German periodicals are ATM: *Archiv für Technisches Messen*, *Feinwerktechnik*, *Regelungstechnische Praxis*, and *Zeitschrift für Instrumentenkunde* (with text in English and German). Important French periodicals include *Mesures, Régulation, Automatisme* and *Instruments & Laboratoires*, a quarterly review of French instruments and technical developments with text in English and French. The Swiss *Microtecnic* is in English, French, and German and is bi-monthly.

Among the journals produced by manufacturing firms are the well-known *Hilger Journal* (Hilger & Watts Ltd.), *Instrument Engineer* (George Kent Ltd.), *Marconi Instrumentation*, and *Muirhead Technique* (Muirhead & Co. Ltd., Beckenham). *Instrumentation* is issued by the United States firm Honeywell Industrial Products Group. Two similar publications are *Instrument and Control Engineering* (London) and *Research Techniques and Instrumentation* (London, Ashbourne Publications). A widely distributed Swedish journal is *Science Tools: the LKB instrument journal* (LKB-Produkter AB, Stockholm).

Abstracts

The major abstracting service in instrumentation covering world literature is *Instrument Abstracts*, compiled by the British Scientific Instrument Research Association and formerly known as their *Bulletin*. The abstracts, published monthly, are arranged by subject and have a monthly author index with annual author and subject indexes.

A weekly service on 5 in. by 8 in. Unisort cards is the American *Instrumentation Abstracts*, which only covers English language literature but does include US patents. Subscriptions can be taken out for each of six categories.

Two sections of the Russian *Referativnyi Zhurnal* are relevant to this chapter: *Izmeritel'naya Tekhnika* deals with measurement technology and *Pribory Tochnoi Mekhaniki Ispytatel'nye Ustanovki* with instrumentation and precision instruments. Particular attention to Japanese literature was paid, naturally, by the section "From the Latest Periodicals" in *Keisoku, Journal of the Society of Instrument Technology, Japan*, which included about 1400 references and abstracts per year from Western as well as Japanese sources. This is now replaced by the *Journal of the Society of Instrument and Control Engineers, Japan*.

The German periodical *ATM: Archiv für Technisches Messen und Industrielle Messtechnik* has a section devoted to about 400 abstracts a year from world literature.

Directories

The Scientific Instrument Manufacturers' Association of Great Britain produces a *British Instruments Data: directory and handbook* (1965) which gives a comprehensive list of British manufacturers and their products. *Instruments, Electronics, Automation, Yearbook and Buyers' Guide* (Morgan Bros.) also covers the field.

Encyclopedias and Dictionaries

Instrument Encyclopedia, compiled by E. W. Battey (London, Herbert, 1958), is both an encyclopedia and a directory and buyers' guide. It also has a list of trade names. Group 20 of the *International Electrotechnical Vocabulary* is concerned with scientific and industrial measuring instruments, and A. F. Dorian's *Six-language Dictionary of Automation, Electronics and Scientific Instruments* (Iliffe, 1962) and the Elsevier *Dictionary of Automation, Computers, Control and Measuring Instruments* (1961) are both useful.

Guides

Two useful guides to the literature are *The Catalogue of Books in the Library of the British Scientific Instrument Research Association* (SIRA, 1960) in 2 volumes, and *Guide to Instrumentation Literature* by J. F. Smith and W. G. Brombacher (Washington, National Bureau of Standards, 1965).

CHAPTER 13

Magnetic and Insulating Materials
UDC 621.315, 621.318

THE advances made in the theory and practice of magnetism and magnetic materials over the past 15 years or so have been considerable. To keep abreast with the latest developments the reader must first consult the periodical literature and select from the large number of articles that appear every year.

But the literature is very much dispersed and there is the need for a consolidation of the most significant papers to save the reader's time. The first standard reference work in the United Kingdom to collate such information is *Permanent Magnets and Magnetism*, edited by D. Hadfield (Iliffe, 1962), with each chapter contributed by a specialist either from industry or the academic world. It has been designed for electrical and mechanical engineers in the user industries, those concerned with the technical and practical aspects of magnetic design and manufacture, and postgraduates and students. Extensive bibliographies accompany each chapter.

Similar in treatment but written from the American viewpoint, and directed towards the engineer, is R. J. Parker and R. J. Studders' *Permanent Magnets and their Application*, Wiley, 1962.

A more extensive work, covering the most diverse aspects of ferromagnetism, ferri-magnetism, and auto-ferromagnetism in insulators as well as in metals, is *Magnetism: a treatise on modern theory and materials*, edited by G. T. Rado and H. Suhl, 4 volumes (New York, Academic Press, 1963–6). While some aspects of the current technological applications are included, the emphasis is on physical characteristics, potentialities and limitations. Another

M

recent work is W. L. Week's *Electromagnetic Theory for Engineering Applications* (New York, Wiley 1964), based on material presented to first-year graduate students at the University of Illinois.

A useful work for the engineer, covering hard and soft materials and their properties, is P. R. Bardell's *Magnetic Materials in the Electric Industry*, 2nd edn. (Macdonald, 1960). It includes chapters on such special devices as sound recorders, non-destructive testers, transductors, and transducers.

A good standard text from the physical standpoint, one that has reached a 3rd edition, is F. Brailsford's *Magnetic Materials* (1960). Published by Methuen in the Monographs on Physical Subjects series, it has good bibliographies within each chapter. Written for the physics student and from the experimental point of view is L. F. Bates's *Modern Magnetism*, now in a 4th edition (Cambridge University Press, 1961). The subject receives detailed treatment in the well illustrated and documented *Ferromagnetism* by Eckert Kneller (Berlin, Springer-Verlag, 1962). Although written in German the book carries an English subject index.

Another area that has seen the introduction of a great number of new materials, resulting from the rapid advances that have been made in synthetic chemistry, is that concerned with insulation. Because of the extensive and scattered literature on the subject, the reader will find very useful F. M. Clark's *Insulating Materials for Design and Engineering Practice* (Wiley, 1962). Materials are classified by types, and properties and stabilities are given, including mechanical, thermal, and electrical behaviour. Data is ignored where there is an absence of clearly defined chemical composition or effective test. There are extensive references.

Periodicals

Much of the periodical information on materials will be found throughout the electrical engineering journals noted in this work. In this particular subject, perhaps, more than any other discussed, the law of "scatter" applies. "Scatter" is the phenomenon of the extremely wide dispersal of information sources for a topic or subject area. Thus the periodicals dealing with metals, plastics, rubber, glass, ceramics, and other materials involved in electrical engineering may all have useful material. Journals devoted to physics, especially applied physics, are also valuable sources. The *British Journal of Applied Physics* (Institute of Physics) and the *Journal of Applied Physics* (American Institute of Physics) are two of the most important. Periodicals such as *Applied Materials Research* (quarterly, London, Heywood & Co. Ltd.) should also be scanned for likely papers. Abstracting and indexing services, of course, are an effective means of collocating distributed source material. *Journal of Materials* (quarterly, ASTM) and *Journal of Materials Science* (quarterly, London, Chapman & Hall) both started in 1966.

Abstracts

To scan world literature adequately for information about materials would involve consultation of several abstracting and and indexing services in appropriate subject fields. For metals there is the comprehensive *ASM Review of Metal Literature*, published monthly by the American Society for Metals, and containing 12000 abstracts (per year) arranged by the special ASM–SLA Classification of Metallurgical Literature. There are services for individual metals such as *Copper Abstracts* (Copper Development Association), *Lead Abstracts* (Lead Development Association), the *Nickel Bulletin*, *Platinum Metals Review*, and *Zinc Abstracts*.

For other materials, as well as *Chemical Abstracts*, there is *Plastics Abstracts* (weekly, Plastic Investigations, Welwyn, Herts. —about 9000 abstracts a year), *Rubbers: RAPRA Abstracts* (Rubber and Plastics Research Association—monthly), *Transactions of the British Ceramic Society* (containing a section of 2500 abstracts a year of world ceramic literature), and *Journal of the American Ceramic Society* (containing a section "Ceramic Abstracts").

Encyclopedias

Two comprehensive works, both American, which will be generally useful are the *Materials Handbook* by G. S. Brady (McGraw-Hill, 9th edn., 1963), an encyclopedia for purchasing agents, engineers, executives, and foremen, covering some 10,000 natural and manufactured products; and *Engineering Materials Handbook*, edited by C. L. Mantell (McGraw-Hill, 1958). *The Encyclopedia of Engineering Materials* by H. R. Clauser and others (New York, Reinhold, 1963) is also valuable.

CHAPTER 14

Electrotechnical Applications
UDC 621.32 to 621.36

THE application of electricity to heating, illumination, traction, and chemical technology is well covered in the published literature and in most cases, by representative societies. Useful books on heating technology include *Industrial Electric Furnaces and Appliances* by V. Paschkis and J. Persson (2nd edn., Interscience, 1960); *Electric Furnaces*, edited by C. A. Otto (Newnes, 1958); and J. J. Barton's *Electric Space Heating: design and practice* (Newnes, 1963). The Institution of Electric Engineers have also published a book on space heating. Other aspects covered by books include radio-frequency heating, and infrared thermal applications.

A good standard work on lighting principles and practice is H. Cotton's *Principles of Illumination* (Chapman & Hall, 1960). Primarily intended for the requirements of the IEE examination syllabus, many chapters go beyond these requirements to meet the needs of the illuminating engineer. Another basic book, although dated, is *Illuminating Engineering* by W. B. Boast, 2nd edn. (McGraw-Hill, 1953).

Societies

The international forum for the science and art of illumination is the International Commission on Illumination, formed in 1900. Progress in various specializations is reported every 4 years by sixteen committees of experts. The proceedings on these conferences are normally published in 4 volumes covering Sources of Radiation, Lighting Technique, Lighting Practice, and Lighting and Traffic. Issued separately is the multilingual glossary *International Lighting Vocabulary* in 2 volumes.

An important national organization is the Illuminating Engineering Society of New York, founded in 1906 to promote the art, science, and technology of artificial and natural lighting in all or any of their branches. Technical committees cover such facets as aviation, colour, daylighting, industrial, motor vehicles, light control standards, testing procedures, etc. The Society's main publication is the monthly *Illuminating Engineering*. Other publications include the *IES Lighting Handbook* (3rd edn., 1959), approved lighting practices over a wide variety of areas, lighting data sheets, and a series of *Technical Reports*. Titles included in this series are *The Calculation of Co-efficients of Utilization* (No. 2), *Lighting during Daylight Hours* (No. 4), and *The Floodlighting of Buildings* (No. 6).

There is also an Illuminating Engineering Society in London. It publishes regularly a monthly *Light and Lighting* and a monthly *Transactions*. The monthly journal carries annually an excellent review of technical developments in Europe, the United States, and Canada. Other IES (London) publications include *The Lighting of Building Sites*, *Lecture Theatres and their Lighting*, and *Lighting for Sport*.

Another organization in the United Kingdom is the Association of Public Lighting Engineers, founded in 1928. Technological progress in lamps and lighting appliances is discussed at annual conferences. The record of these and other meetings is published in the official quarterly journal *Public Lighting*.

The representative international body for heat engineering is the International Union for Electroheat, founded in 1953 and one of the members of the International Engineering Organization. Permanent liaison is maintained between member countries on all matters connected with the industrial application of electroheat, excluding the commercial aspect. In addition to the Transactions of various international congresses, the Union publishes through the German Committee for Electroheat the annual *Jahrbuch der Elektrowärme*.

Representing electrochemists at a supra-national level is the International Committee of Electro-Chemical Thermodynamics and Kinetics, founded in 1949. It publishes from time to time proceedings of Colloquia and *Comptes Rendus*. The Committee's regular publication is the bi-monthly *Electrochimica Acta*, an international journal of pure and applied electrochemistry (since 1959).

Also important in this field is the Electrochemical Society of New York which was formed in 1902 as a purely American body but became international in scope in 1930. Its aims are to advance the theory and practice of electrochemistry, electrometallurgy, electrothermics, and associated topics. Specialist divisions cover Batteries, Corrosion, Electric Insulation, Electrodeposition, Electronics, etc. The Society publishes regularly a monthly *Journal*, which includes abstracts of papers presented at the Society's meetings, and *Semiconductor Abstracts*. It also publishes separately the proceedings of the various technical symposia.

Periodicals

Periodicals on electrotechnological subjects are many and range widely over related disciplines such as transportation engineering, civil engineering, and electrochemistry.

Lighting

We have already seen that the two major societies of Britain and America produce important journals in addition to other material. The Illuminating Engineering Society of New York has been responsible for *Illuminating Engineering* since its beginning in 1906. This monthly journal also carried abstracts, references, notes on trade literature, etc. As well as the British journal *Public Lighting* mentioned earlier, there is the Street and Highway Safety Lighting Bureau's quarterly *Street and Highway Lighting*, published in Cleveland, Ohio. From Japan comes the *Illuminating Engineering Institute of Japan Journal* (in Japanese but with summaries in English); from France the well-established

Lux; la Revue de l'Eclairage, published 5 times a year in Paris; and from Germany a periodical of great use, *Lichttechnik*, published monthly since 1949 and containing abstracts, patents and market information, and book reviews.

There are several periodicals dealing with electrotechnology generally, but they are mostly from east European sources, for example *Elektrotechnika*, published monthly in Hungary with summaries in English, German, and Russian. The Czechoslovakian journal *Elektrotechnicky Obzor* was started in 1910 and contains summaries in English, French, German, and Russian. It is covered by a number of indexing and abstracting services. *The Electrotechnical Journal of Japan*, published quarterly, is in English, however. Another useful foreign publication is the Dutch *Electrotechniek*, published fortnightly.

Heating

Specifically applicable to this technology is *Electric Heat and Air Conditioning*, an American publication which appears bi-monthly (Heating Publishers Inc., New York). *Industrial Heating* (monthly, Pittsburgh), *Institution of Heating and Ventilating Engineers Journal* (monthly, The Institute, London), and *Heating, Piping and Air Conditioning* (monthly, Chicago) are other periodicals dealing with the topic of electric heating in addition to other kinds of heating.

Electrochemistry

Periodicals on electrochemistry (some of which have already mentioned under Societies) include:

Electroanalytical Abstracts.

Electrochemical Society Journal, The Society, New York, monthly.

Electrochemical Technology, bi-monthly, The Society, New York.

Electrochimica Acta (International Committee for Electrochemical Thermodynamics and Kinetics), published by Pergamon, monthly.

Journal of Electroanalytical Chemistry, Elsevier, Netherlands.
Soviet Electrochemistry, English language translation of *Elektrokhimiya*, Consultants Bureau, New York, monthly.

Abstracts

The Illuminating Engineering Society's periodical *Light and Lighting* has a special section of "Lighting Abstracts" reviewing American and west European literature on such aspects as photometry; light sources, fittings and equipment; and lighting applications. *Building Science Abstracts* covers heating and lighting, while the *Library Bulletin of the Heating and Ventilation Research Association* contains about 500 abstracts a year. Generally, however, these subjects are less well provided for than most others in electrical engineering.

Beyond the general electrical engineering guides for traction and electric transport it will be necessary to consult services catering for road, rail and air transport. British Railways' *Monthly Review of Technical Literature* may be useful and so also *International Railway Documentation* (Int. Railways Union) and *Railway Research and Engineering News* (Railroad Engineering Index Institute, Amsterdam). There are several aeronautical information services of which two may be mentioned: *Index Aeronauticus* (Ministry of Aviation) and *International Aerospace Abstracts* (A.I.A.A.). These two sources will guide readers to information on electric space propulsion in particular.

Direct Energy Conversion Literature Abstracts (mentioned earlier) covers the subject of thermoelectricity and for electrochemistry *Chemical Abstracts* is valuable as are *Chemisches Zentralblatt* and *Bulletin Signalétique* (Section 7). *Denki Kagaku, Journal of the Electrochemical Society of Japan*, has about 1800 references a year to world literature and the *Journal of Electroanalytical Chemistry*, published monthly by Elsevier, Amsterdam, has an abstracts section.

CHAPTER 15

Electromagnetic Waves and Applications
UDC 621.37

THE theory and practice of electromagnetic waves, which has exercised the ingenuity of the scientist since the end of the nineteenth century, continues to be an area of rapid development. Like other aspects of transmission and communication technology it is difficult to keep up to date with current developments through the use of textbooks alone. Nevertheless there are some good basic publications for various levels of readership.

The fundamental basis of electromagnetism, of course, is still in the classics — Clerk Maxwell, Max Planck, T. De Donder, Mason and Weaver, Sir James Jeans, Oliver Heaviside, J. A. Stratton, W. R. Smyth, etc. A useful bibliography of more than 70 basic works is included in J. van Bladel's *Electromagnetic Fields* (1964), published in the McGraw-Hill Electrical and Electronic Engineering series. In addition to general mathematical background requirements, this book deals with the calculation of electric and magnetic fields in the presence of ponderable bodies at rest. With coverage of microwave techniques, antennae, waveguides, etc., it is a useful publication for the radio engineer whose traditional background is insufficient for understanding these new techniques.

Other books from the same publisher written for lower level requirements include S. Seely's *Introduction to Electromagnetic Fields* (1958), R. F. Harrington's *Introduction to Electromagnetic Engineering* (1958), and R. V. Longmuir's *Electromagnetic Fields and Waves* (1961).

Another series worthy of consultation is Pergamon's *International Series of Monographs on Electromagnetic Waves*. Pergamon Press are also responsible for the graduate text *Theory of Electromagnetism* (1964) by D. S. Jones of Keele University, complete with exercises to help the application of theory to particular problems. At the same level is W. L. Week's *Electromagnetic Theory for Engineering Applications* (Wiley, 1964).

Applications of the electromagnetic system, involving the behaviour of networks and their parameters, waveguides and filters, amplifiers, frequency analysis, etc., have a representative literature which is far too voluminous for specific treatment in this book. There are, however, a number of good general texts and several reputable series.

The Theory of Networks and Lines by J. I. Potter and S. Fich, published by Prentice-Hall, 1963, is a textbook on network analysis, design, and synthesis. It requires, however, a preliminary knowledge of circuits and basic mathematics.

The increased complexity of modern electrical systems and the requirements of maintaining small volume, low weight, and high reliability, have led to the development of network synthesis, a technique that often replaces analysis procedures. Two books from Wiley cover these new techniques *Network Synthesis* by D. F. Tuttle (1958) and the more recent *Procedures of Modern Network Synthesis* by W. C. Yengst (1964).

The reader who requires a lucid introduction to the basic principles of networks and associated topics is well recommended to refer to specific titles in Methuen's *Monographs on Physical Subjects*. Books included in this series are *Elements of Pulse Circuits*, *Heaviside's Electric Circuit Theory*, *Magnetic Amplifiers*, *Wave Filters*, *Wave Guides*, and *Wave Mechanics*.

Another very reputable series, but giving more advanced and extensive treatment, is the *Electrical and Electronic Engineering Series*, under the general editorship of F. E. Terman and published by McGraw-Hill. Relevant titles in this series include:

    W. CAUER. *Synthesis of Linear Communication Networks*,
       2 volumes, 2nd edn., 1958.

W. H. CHEN. *Linear Network Design and Synthesis*, 1964.

W. L. HARMAN and D. W. LYTLE. *Electrical and Mechanical Networks*, 1962.

L. WEINBERG. *Network Analysis and Synthesis*, 1962.

Periodicals and Abstracts

The components, devices, and systems dealt with in this chapter will mostly be covered in the periodical and abstract literature described in other chapters, notably those on electronics and telecommunications. There are several journals, however, concerned with microwaves: *Microwave Engineering* (London, Ashbourne Publications, Alberon Gardens, NW 11, monthly, 1965–), *Microwave Journal* (Dedham, Mass., Horizon House, monthly), *Microwaves* (New York, Hayden Microwaves Corporation, monthly), and *IEEE Transactions on Microwave Theory and Techniques* (bi-monthly).

Another Horizon House publication is *Solid State Design*, which covers communications and data equipment and in which microwave applications figure strongly. *New Electronic Components* (Pergamon Press, bi-monthly) covers new products, materials and, processes; *Electronic Components* (monthly, London, United Trade Press) includes R & D news, new publications, new products, and technical, rather than research level, papers; *Proceedings of the Electronic Components Conference* are sponsored annually by the IEEE, the Electronic Industries Association and the American Society for Quality Control. The IEEE also has its *Transactions on Electron Devices* (monthly), and *IEEE Transactions on Parts, Materials and Packaging* replaces, from June 1965, the former *IEEE Transactions on Component Parts* and *IEEE Transactions on Product Engineering and Production*. The *IEEE Journal of Quantum Electronics* (monthly, 1965–) contains much on laser applications including a laser bibliography in June and August 1965 issues. A fairly new title is *Frontiers–Lasers/Masers* (1964– , monthly) published in Ballwyn, Mo., USA. *Applied Optics* (Optical Society of America) has an annual supplement on chemical lasers.

There is a new loose-leaf abstracting service called *Laser/Maser International* published monthly by Pacific Impex Co., Vancouver, Canada. Both this and *Laser Abstracts* (Lowry Cocroft Abstracts, Evanston, Ill.,) was started in 1964. The latter is on cards and is for physicists and engineers engaged in research and development in the laser field.

CHAPTER 16

Electronics
UDC 621.38

IN A relatively short space of time many branches of electronics which were at one time the domain of pure science are now of current technological importance. It is a subject of such wide implications as to concern all kinds of engineering and laboratory work. It is desirable, however, not to lose sight of the fundamental work upon which much of this current activity is based. The classic work is *Conduction of Electricity through Gases* by Sir J. T. Thomson and G. P. Thomson (Cambridge University Press), which ran to 3 editions, the first in 1903, the third in 2 volumes published in 1928 and 1933. Particularly useful for its coverage of earlier significant work is the bibliography of several hundred titles dating from 1859.

Bibliographies

The bibliographical guide to electronics by C. K. Moore and K. J. Spencer has already been mentioned and there are two additional bibliographies of value. Giving comprehensive coverage of full-length papers in journals for the period 1930–50 is the *Bibliography on Physical Electronics*, compiled by W. B. Nottingham and others, and published for the Massachusetts Institute of Technology by Addison-Wesley, 1954. It also includes important papers published from 1900. More recent is *The Electronics Book List*, edited by G. W. A. Dummer and J. M. Robertson (United Trade Press, 1964). The list, which is unannotated, includes selected books in all those fields likely to be of

ELECTRON TUBES: BASIC PHENOMENA OF ELECTRON FLOW 2-89

Field-emission Point. The fabrication of field-emission points has been described by W. P. Dyke et al. (17). Electrolytic etching seems to give better field points than other methods of creation, such as mechanical grinding and chemical etching. The emitter point has frequently been made of about 0.005-in.-diameter tungsten wire, which is spotted by a cross-weld to the end of a tungsten "hair pin" filament. After mounting, the 0.005-in. wire is etched by using an electrolytic bath of normal NaOH. The other electrode may be a loop of nickel wire. A 60-cycle alternating potential of about 10 volts is connected to the cell. In vacuum processing a field emitter it has been found that flashing a freshly etched point to above 2800°C causes irregularities in the point to be smoothed and the apex becomes somewhat rounded. Points created in this manner and heated to 2000°C during operation as pulsed field emitter have lasted for several hundred hours.

Detail techniques of construction of the oxide-coated cathode are given by Hermann and Wagener (1), of the nickelate cathode by Edwards and Smith (13), and of the tungsten field-emission point by W. P. Dyke et al. (17). For further information about fabrication, these references and others given in the table are highly recommended.

REFERENCES

1. Hermann, G., and S. Wagener: "The Oxide Coated Cathode," vols. 1 and 2, Chapman & Hall, Ltd., London, 1951.
2. Eisenstein, A.: "Advances in Electronics," vol. 1, Academic Press, Inc., New York, 1948.
3. Wright, D. A.: *Proc. Inst. Elec. Eng.*, **100**, III:125 (1953).
4. Lemmens, H. J., M. T. Jansen, and R. Loosjes: *Philips Tech. Rev.*, **11**:341 (1950).
5. Levi, R.: *J. Appl. Phys.*, **26**:639 (1955).
6. Lafferty, J. M.: *J. Appl. Phys.*, **22**:299 (1951).
7. Weinreich, O. A.: *J. Appl. Phys.*, **20**:1256 (1949).
8. Mesnard, G.: *J. phys. radium*, **14**:179 (1953).
9. Langmuir, I.: *J. Franklin Inst.*, **217**:543 (1934).

Fig. 31. Cockrell's *Industrial Electronics Handbook.* (Copyright McGraw-Hill Book Co., Inc. Used by permission.)

interest to electronic engineers. Headings cover components, dictionaries and encyclopedias, reference books, tables and formulae, textbooks, handbooks, etc.

Handbooks

Several handbooks on electronics are available. *The Industrial Electronics Handbook*, edited by W. D. Cockrell (McGraw-Hill, 1958), is very well produced with many illustrations, graphs, tables, and bibliographies (Fig. 31). It begins with mathematics and theory and includes components, power sources, basic circuits and their applications, instruments and computers, equipment, mechanical design, user requirements, and technical information sources. An older reference work, but still referred to, is the *Industrial Electronics Reference Book*, compiled by the Westinghouse Electric Corporation and published by Wiley (1948). For the electronic equipment designer is the *Electronic Designers' Handbook* by R. W. Landee and others (McGraw-Hill, 1957), and a publication by the Institution of Electrical Engineers entitled *Components and Materials used in Electronic Engineering* (1965).

Published in Britain, but with scope and arrangement quite different from Cockrell, is L. E. C. Hughes' *Electronic Engineers' Reference Book* (2nd edn., Heywood, 1959). It excludes radar, radio, television, telecommunications, wave-filters, and all service equipment, but includes discussion on permanent and soft magnets, other materials, vibrations, computing, automation, photoelectrics, heating, transmission, electrolytics, etc. (Fig. 32). It contains numerous tables.

Factual information on components in extensive use in US military electronic equipment is given in the *Electronic Components Handbook* by K. Henney and C. Walsh, sponsored by the Wright Air Development Center (McGraw-Hill, 1957-9). This handbook is in 3 volumes: I, resistors, capacitors, relays, switches, etc; II, power sources and convertors, fuses and circuit breakers, electrical indicating instruments, etc.; III, transformers and inductors, connectors, etc.

47. TRANSISTORS

471. Transistors—General

1. History of transistors starts from the discovery of rectifying action in solids by Munck Af. Roschenschold in 1835 (a). This discovery and its application to detection of radio waves was not used until about 1906 when the cat's whisker type of detector using carborundum (silicon carbide SiC) was developed. This is the first use of silicon, which now is used in transistors suitable for high temperature operation.

In 1924 Lossev (b) obtained amplification and oscillation using point contacts with various materials such as zincite and carborundum.

About 1930 the physical theory of conduction in solids was published by Wilson (c) and Mott (d). The advent of radar using crystal rectifiers gave an impetus to their further study. The silicon point contact rectifier was ideal for ultra high frequency detection, but had low reverse voltage limitations. Germanium diodes were found to be more suitable as high reverse voltage rectifiers. In parallel with this work the study of doping or adding other elements, such as tin or boron, was developed.

It was then discovered that rectification can be obtained at the junction of two types of semiconductors (p–n junction). During this period the point contact diode became a reliable circuit element.

(a) Munck Af. Roschenschold. *Ann. Pogg.* **34**, 437 (1835).
(b) Lossev. See T. R. Scott. *Transistors and other Crystal Valves.*
(c) A. H. Wilson. *Proc. Roy. Soc. A*, **133** (1931).
(d) N. F. Mott. *Proc. Roy. Soc. A*, **171** (1939).

2. Post-war. At the Bell Telephone Laboratories the study of high reverse voltage diodes was concentrated on the effect of surface charges on diode characteristics. Bardeen and Brattain (a) found that they could control the surface charge density, and thus the characteristics by using an electrolyte in contact with the surface of the diode semi-conductor material. They then investigated the effect of an electrode close to the first contact and found the same controlling effect. The device was named *transistor*. The two contacts they called *emitter* and *collector* respectively. Oscillation and amplification were demonstrated.

(a) J. Bardeen and W. H. Brattain. ' The transistor, a semiconductor Triode.' *Phys. Rev.* **74**, 230 (1948).
See also *Phys. Rev.* **75**, 208–225 (1949).

3. Solid state. The discovery of transistor action caused a great intensification in the study of solid state devices, and in 1949 the Bell Telephone Laboratory announced the p–n junction type transistor (a). Circuitry using point contact transistors was then well established, and it was not long before the behaviour of junction transistors, at least in low frequency circuits, was understood. Early junction transistors suffered from extreme variation and instability of parameters, the latter due to poor sealing of the junction. The improvement in purification techniques and the use of hermetic seals has improved the situation

813

FIG. 32. Hughes' *Electronic Engineers' Reference Book*. (By permission of Iliffe Books Ltd.)

Data covering all kinds of manufacturers equipment is normally available by application to the appropriate company. A good example is the *Philips Handbook* issued in 5 volumes by the Electronic Tube Division. These extensive loose-leaf publications give full details of every valve made by that company.

Recent publications of value as guides to components include G. W. A. Dummer's *Modern Electronic Components* (2nd edn., 1966, Pitman) and *British Miniature Electronic Components Data Annual* (Pergamon).

Treatises and Textbooks

As an authoritative introduction to current thought on the subject *Foundations of Future Electronics* (McGraw-Hill, University of California Engineering and Sciences Extension Series, 1962) is a very useful compilation for the working engineer and the applied scientist. Chapters on solid-state physics, plasma physics, electrons in vacuum, environment, etc., are by outstanding authorities on those subjects.

There are far too many textbooks on electronics to enumerate; the selected titles that follow are to be regarded as good examples only. A good background for the understanding of current devices in use is provided by J. D. Ryder's *Electronic Fundamentals and Applications* (Pitman), now in its 3rd edition, 1964. It is an integrated treatment of solid-state devices and the older vacuum and gaseous forms of active electronic devices. Recent developments covered include parametric amplifiers, and masers and lasers.

Design primarily for qualified scientists and engineers who are not electrical specialists are two recent books by E. E. Zepler and S. W. Punnett of Southampton University: *Electronic Devices and Networks* and *Electronic Circuit Techniques* (Blackie, 1963). Covering more or less the same field is J. M. Carroll's *Electron Devices and Circuits* (McGraw-Hill, 1962).

Two recent first-year degree texts are B. V. Rollin's *Introduction to Electronics* (Oxford University Press, 1964) and E. J. Angelo's *Electronic Circuits: a unified treatment of vacuum tubes and transistors* (2nd edn., 1964, McGraw-Hill).

Encyclopedias and Dictionaries

This very vigorous technological field is fortunately well catered for in monolingual and multilingual dictionaries. In the well-known Elsevier series is W. E. Clason's *Elsevier's Dictionary of Electronics and Waveguides*, with Swedish and Russian supplements, published in 1957, second edition, 1966.

A new polyglot dictionary is *Dictionary of Electrical Engineering, Telecommunications and Electronics* by W. Goedecke (Brandstetter Verlag, Wiesbaden), of which Vol. 1, *German–English–French*, appeared in 1964. The Consultants Bureau, New York, have published a *German–English, English–German Electronics Dictionary* by Charles J. Hyman, which is concise and current and is the first of a series of specialized technical dictionaries. Earlier, in 1957, the Bureau brought out a *Russian–English Glossary of Electronics and Physics*, which also contains information on circuit notation, US equivalents for Russian vacuum tubes, and Russian components. The US Department of the Army issued an *English–Russian, Russian–English Electronics Dictionary* in 1956 which contains about 22,000 Russian terms and abbreviations.

Various concise glossaries of electronics are also available. One of the most authoritative is the *IRE Dictionary of Electronics Terms and Symbols* (1961), published by the then (see p. 66) Institute of Radio Engineers and compiled from IRE Standards. Two handy British publications are the *Dictionary of Electronics* by Harley Carter (Newnes, 2nd edn., 1963) and *A Dictionary of Electronics* by S. Handel (Penguin Books, 1962). Rather bigger is the American *Modern Dictionary of Electronics* by R. F. Graf (Howard W. Sams, 2nd edn., 1963).

A work compiled by two authors who between them have written many useful books on electrical engineering is *Electronics and Nucleonics Dictionary* by Nelson M. Cooke and John Markus (McGraw-Hill, 1960) dealing with over 13,000 terms.

Among encyclopedic dictionaries and encyclopedias is the *Encyclopedic Dictionary of Electronics and Nuclear Engineering*

Power supply, high-voltage

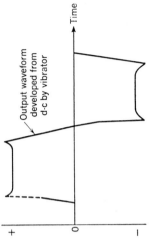

transients produced both in the attenuating current supply and within the vibrator device is filtered by the filter section shown at the output.

Fig. 3. Vibrator output characteristic.

Power supply, voltage-regulated. A power supply including rectifier, filter, and stabilizer used to

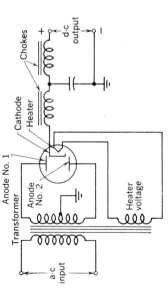

Fig. 1. A Full wave high voltage power supply.

negative with respect to the cathode. It may consist of a resistor, a resistor in shunt with a capacitor, a battery, a bias cell, a power supply or other circuit. **Syn.** C-power supply.

Fɪɢ. 33.   From Robert I. Sarbacher's *Encyclopedic Dictionary of Electronics and Nuclear Engineering.* (Copyright 1959. Prentice-Hall, Inc., USA.)

(Fig. 33) by Robert I. Sarbacher (Prentice-Hall, 1959), an heroic work for one individual but making wise use of definitions prepared and approved by various professional societies. The *Encyclopedia of Electronics* edited by Charles Susskind (Fig. 34), however, is a compendium of many authors and each article is signed. This work was published by the Reinhold Publishing Corporation, New York, in 1962. Articles are arranged alphabetically under specific headings, but a plan is included showing the relationship of the headings used to enable the searcher to recall other relevant material that might have been missed. Bibliographies are also included. *The International Dictionary of Physics and Electronics*, 2nd edn., edited by W. C. Michels (Van Nostrand, 1961), also has many contributors and contains multilingual indexes.

Organizations

The two principal electrical institutions in the United Kingdom and in the United States, described in an earlier chapter, are just as much concerned with electronic developments as with other aspects of electrical engineering. The Institute of Radio Engineers which extended its coverage to electronics in 1964 must also be considered. One organization, however, that is specifically involved in this area is the National Electronics Research Council, formed in London in 1964 to co-ordinate the total electronics research effort in Great Britain, possibly extending later to Commonwealth countries. A valuable publication is the Council's quarterly *NERC Review* containing brief accounts of NERC projects, notes of other research achievements and work in progress, and notes on research reports recently issued.

A 3-year project of probable future significance for the electronics research worker is the development of a system of Selective Dissemination of Information (SDI). Operating on a weekly basis the system will supply references of English-language periodical articles, reports, and conference papers to a user group of 800 or more academic, industrial, and government

539 NOISE CHARACTERIZATION AND MEASUREMENT

the positions of light atoms, particularly hydrogen atoms and hydrogen bonds in electron density contour maps of hydrides, ice and salts, ammonium salts, and organic compounds; (2) problems such as are often met in alloy systems, which require a distinction to be made between atoms of neighboring atomic numbers, and which have closely similar scattering amplitudes for x-rays; and (3) investigations of magnetic materials, in which advantage is taken of the additional scattering of neutrons by atoms which possess magnetic moments.

Attention is called to an entirely different analytical application of thermal neutrons, namely, the activation of radioactive isotopes in samples irradiated with these neutrons, and the detection of these radioactive species with extreme sensitiveness. For this purpose, neutron activation cross-section

Amplifier Noise

Currently, there are two figures of merit in popular use to describe the noise performance of an amplifier. One is called the *noise figure* of the amplifier, for which the symbol F is used, and the other is the effective *noise temperature*, or T_e of the amplifier. The latter description has evolved in recent years with the advent of the very low-noise microwave amplifiers such as the maser and parametric amplifier because it was generally felt that a more graphic representation was needed for these devices. The basic difficulty with the more widely accepted *noise figure* was its asymptotic approach to a value of unity for devices with very low noise.

The noise figure is defined as the ratio of the signal-to-noise power ratio at the input of the amplifier to that at the output:

FIG. 34. Susskind's *Encyclopedia of Electronics*. (By permission of the Reinhold Publishing Corporation, Book Division, New York.)

research workers. The key part of the project is the compilation of user profiles and the matching of these with indexed documents. A weekly information bulletin will be issued consisting of a complete print-out of the information material received in the system during the previous week.

Semiconductor Electronics (UDC 621.382)

Since the invention of the transistor in 1947 there has been phenomenal growth in the research effort devoted to this branch of technology. It has resulted in a very large literature — journal and review articles, reports, etc. It is also well represented by abstracting services and progress reviews, for example, *Solid State Physics* (from 1955); *Progress in Semiconductors* (from 1956); and *Semiconductor Abstracts*, compiled by the Battelle Memorial Institute and published annually by Wiley, New York, since 1953.

In addition to Moore and Spencer's excellent bibliographical guide, other useful compilations include the catalogue of technical reports on work sponsored by the US Government, available from the Office of Technical Services (see p. 95) and N. L. Meyrick's *Fifteen Years of Semiconducting Materials and Transistors* issued by the Newmarket Transistor Co. Ltd., 1958.

Much of the latest development is reported from time to time at various conferences, both national and international, e.g. meetings of the Institution of Electrical Engineers and the Institute of Electrical and Electronic Engineers; the Institute of Physics' Semiconductor Conference of 1962 at Exeter; the 3rd International Conference on Advances in Semiconductor Science, 1958; and the International Conference on Semiconductor Physics at Prague, 1960.

Although it is a rapidly changing field with processes soon becoming obsolete, there are a number of fundamental principles whose soundness has been well demonstrated and tested for validity. An outstanding work covering these principles is *Transistor Technology*, edited by H. E. Bridgers, F. J. Biondi, and others, in 3 volumes, 1958 (Princeton, NJ, Van Nostrand).

Another very useful reference book is the *Handbook of Semiconductor Electronics*, edited by L. P. Hunter, 2nd edn., 1962 (McGraw-Hill). This work covers physics; technology; circuit applications of transistors, diodes and photocells; and includes methods of circuit analysis and measurements of semi-conductor device parameters. Important is the comprehensive bibliography (162 pages) arranged in chronological and author order.

There are a number of good texts on the physics of semi-conductor devices, an excellent introduction being D. A. Wright's *Semiconductors* in the Methuen Monographs on Physical Subjects series. A fourth edition was published in 1966.

Other titles:

> EVANS, J. *Fundamental Principles of Transistors*, 2nd edn., London, Heywood, 1962.
>
> SMITH, R. A. *Semiconductors*. Cambridge University Press, 1959.
>
> NUSSBAUM, A. *Semiconductor Device Physics*. Prentice-Hall International Series of Electrical Engineering, 1962.
>
> MOLL, J. L. *Physics of Semiconductors*. McGraw-Hill, 1964. An advanced level textbook.

The chemical viewpoint is presented in *Semiconductors*, edited by N. B. Hannay and published in the American Chemical Society's Monograph Series by Reinhold, 1959.

Useful textbooks covering theory and practice for engineers include:

> SURINA, T. and HERRICK, C. *Semiconductor Electronics*, Holt, Rinehart & Winston, 1964.
>
> SHEA, R. F. (Editor) *Transistor Circuit Engineering*, 1957 (contains over 400 references); and a companion volume, *Transistor Applications*. New York, Wiley, 1964.
>
> SHIVE, J. N. *The Properties, Physics and Design of Semiconductor Devices*, Princeton, NJ, Van Nostrand, 1959.

Two good introductory books are K. W. Cattermole's *Transistor Circuits*, 2nd edn., 1964 (London, Heywood) and E. H. Cooke-Yarborough's *An Introduction to Transistor Circuits*, 2nd edn., 1960 (London, Oliver & Boyd).

Periodicals

Periodicals on electronics appear to enjoy a fairly changeable life: new ones constantly appear while old ones, even apparently flourishing ones like *British Communications and Electronics* die, or are amalgamated or change their identity in some way.

At research level there is *International Journal of Electronics* published monthly by Taylor and Francis Ltd., London, and formerly known as *Journal of Electronics and Control*.

For news of the industry there is a newspaper of electronics and communication — *Electronics Weekly* (London, Heywood-Temple) which includes business news. *Electronics* (fortnightly, New York, McGraw-Hill) is a wide-ranging news and technical journal covering all aspects of the subject. Similar in aims is *Canadian Electronics Engineering* (Toronto, Maclean-Hunter, monthly). *International Electronics* (New York, Johnston, monthly) is published for circulation outside the United States as an export aid and is also available in Spanish as *Electronica Internacional*.

Many of the publications of the professional groups of the Institute of Electrical and Electronics Engineers deal with various aspects of electronics. These include *IEEE Transactions on Aerospace*; *Aerospace and Navigational Electronics*; *Antennas and Propagation*; *Applications and Industry*; *Audio*; *Bio-Medical Engineering*; *Broadcast and Television Receivers*; *Broadcasting*; *Circuit Theory*; *Communications and Electronics*; *Geoscience Electronics*; *Human Factors in Electronics*; *Industrial Electronics*; *Military Electronics*; *Reliability*; *Space Electronics and Telemetry*; and *Vehicular Communications*.

The following titles are also useful in their various ways: *Electronic Applications*; *Electronic Design*; *Electronic Engineering*; *Electronic Equipment News*; *Electronic Industries*; *Electronic Products*; *Electronics and Communications*; *Electronics and Communications in Japan*; *Electronics and Power*; *Electronics Illustrated*; *Electronics World*.

Abstracts

An important and useful abstracts service in electronics with special reference to communications was compiled by the Radio Research Station of the former DSIR and was published monthly as *Abstracts and References* in the Iliffe publication *Electronic Technology* and also in the *Proceedings of the Institute of Radio Engineers.* Unfortunately, after appearing regularly since 1923, it ceased to be compiled in 1964.

A comparatively recent service is *Electronics and Communications Abstracts*, published bi-monthly since September 1961 by the Multi-Science Publishing Co., Brentwood, Essex (now monthly). Between 5000 and 10,000 abstracts from world literature are published each year and arranged by a subject classification. There is an annual subject, author, and patent number index. *Electronics Express*, published 12 times a year in New York (International Physical Index), covers some 98 Russian technical journals and includes complete papers and exerpts as well as abstracts.

A Dutch service, *Electrotechniek, Literatuuroverzicht*, appearing on a semi-monthly basis, publishes about 650 abstracts annually in Dutch, English, or German and includes reports in the material abstracted. It covers electronics, telecommunication, computers, and control systems.

CHAPTER 17

Telecommunication Engineering
UDC 621.39

THE important organization in this field is the International Telecommunication Union, Geneva, a Specialized Agency of the United Nations with a membership of 124 countries. It aims to co-ordinate the work of technical facilities and their efficient operation. It is responsible for the regulations which govern the operation of telegraphy, telephony, and radio around the world.

There are three permanent bodies — the International Frequency Registration Board for the assignment of frequencies; the International Telegraph and Telephone Consultative Committee for the study of technical, operational and tariff matters; and the International Radio Consultative Committee.

ITU issues a great number of publications including service documents (lists of radio stations, telegraph offices, radio call signs, frequencies, etc.), the proceedings of special and regional conferences, statistics, maps, charts, and tables. International operators will find useful the *Vocabulary of Basic Terms used in Line Transmission* and *Phrases most frequently used in the International Telephone Service*. Regular publications include the monthly *Telecommunication Journal* and a monthly summary of monitoring information.

Details of available publications are given both in a list published by the Union and in the *United Nations Document Index*.

In the case of the receiver, 1 volt applied from a 900-ohm source will produce an acoustic pressure of about 30 db greater than a microbar at the ear of the listener.

5. Side Tone. The transformer or induction coil serves two main purposes: (1) by proper choice of winding ratios, it helps to establish optimum impedance relationships

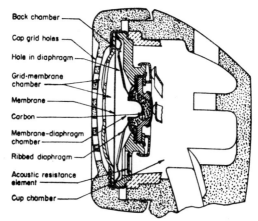

Back chamber
Cap grid holes
Hole in diaphragm
Grid-membrane chamber
Membrane
Carbon
Membrane-diaphragm chamber
Ribbed diaphragm
Acoustic resistance element
Cup chamber

Fig. 5. Telephone transmitter.

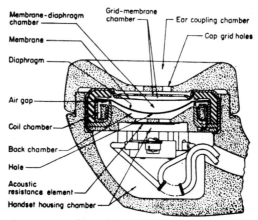

Membrane-diaphragm chamber
Membrane
Diaphragm
Air gap
Coil chamber
Back chamber
Hole
Acoustic resistance element
Handset housing chamber

Grid-membrane chamber
Ear coupling chamber
Cap grid holes

Fig. 6. Telephone receiver.

between the different elements of the telephone set and the line; and (2) it provides a degree of directional selectivity and tends to lessen the sound which returns through the receiver to the ear when speaking into the transmitter. Thus it minimizes the *side tone* when using the telephone set.

Abstracts

The abstracting services mentioned earlier for the wider fields of electrical engineering and electronics will, of course, contain much relevant material.

Specialized abstracts and indexes include: *Telecommunication Journal*, published monthly by the International Telecommunications Union (in English, French, and Spanish editions), which has a Review section giving references to world literature by means of listing tables of contents of journals arranged by country; and *International Broadcast Engineer* (monthly, Television Mail Ltd., London) has an abstracts section and gives regular British and American Patents news.

Another journal giving contents list of other periodicals is *Revista de Telecommunicación*, published quarterly by the Dirección General de Telecommunicación, Madrid.

The *Bulletin Signalétique des Télécommunications*, which is published monthly by the Societé de la Revue d'Optique, Paris, contains about 12,000 abstracts a year from journals of all countries. The German periodical *Frequenz* (monthly) carries about 150 references a year to patents and provides abstracts of English-language and European books. Another German periodical, *NTZ Nachrichtentechnik*, gives UDC numbers to its abstracts from European and English-language sources as does *Nachrichtentechnik*, which also includes Slavic literature and patents in its coverage. The Swiss bi-monthly journal *Radio TV Service* abstracts French, German, and English-language books.

Most comprehensive of all, but in Russian, is *Referativnyi Zhurnal: Radiotekhnika i Elektrosvyaz*, which altogether carries about 45,000 abstracts a year on radio engineering, electronics, and components. A number of other Russian and east European journals also have useful abstracts or review sections.

FIG. 35 (*opposite*). Henney's *Radio Engineering Handbook*. (Copyright McGraw-Hill Book Co. Inc. Used by permission.)

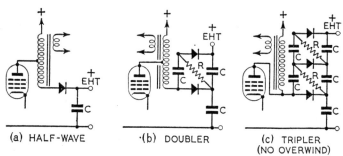

(a) HALF-WAVE   ·(b) DOUBLER   (c) TRIPLER
(NO OVERWIND)

Fig. 23.—Half-wave, Doubler, and Tripler Pulse-driven
Rectifier Multipliers.

E.H.T. by Half-wave Rectification from Mains Transformer

The main advantage of this arrangement is the good voltage regulation which can be obtained.   The disadvantages are the size and cost of
the mains transformer and the reservoir capacitor.

Table 6.—E.H.T. Half-wave Rectifiers (Sine-wave Input)

Rectifier	Approximate E.H.T. Output Voltage		R.M.S. Input Voltage	C * (μF)
	At 100 μA Load	At 2 mA Load		
36EHT30	1,050	1,000	810	0·5
36EHT45	1,575	1,500	1,220	0·25
36EHT60	2,100	2,000	1,620	0·25
36EHT100	3,500	3,250	2,700	0·1
36EHT160	5,600	5,300	4,320	0·1
36EHT200	7,000	6,600	5,400	0·1
36EHT240	8,400	7,900	6,480	0·05

* The values given for C are for 50-c/s supplies.   For other frequencies C
should be varied in inverse proportion to the frequency.   Capacitance may be
reduced for 100 μA load.

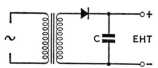

Fig. 24.—E.H.T. Half-wave Rectifier (Sine-wave Input).

Radiocommunication

The outstanding reference work on this subject is the *Radio Engineering Handbook*, edited by K. Henney (Fig. 35) and in its 5th edition (McGraw-Hill, 1959). This is a comprehensive working manual with concise information of every branch, compiled by experts in each field. Each chapter includes extensive references. A smaller compilation but more recent is the *Radio and Television Engineers' Reference Book* (Fig. 36), edited by J. P. Hawker and W. E. Pannett, 4th edn. (Newnes, 1963). Fifty contributors cover all types of equipment and components.

An older work, particularly useful for retrospective searches, is the *Radio Designer's Handbook*, edited by F. Langford-Smith, 4th edn., 1953 (new impression with addenda, 1963, Iliffe). Over 3000 references give comprehensive coverage of radio receivers and audio amplifiers. Another useful bibliography of over 350 references covering the period 1893–1951 is included in A. T. Starr's *Radio and Radar Technique* (Pitman, 1953).

The experimental and design engineer is well catered for. In preparation is the 3rd edition of E. E. Zepler's *The Technique of Radio Design* (Chapman & Hall), and it is particularly concerned with the development and testing of all types of radio apparatus. First published in 1943 and recently revised is *Radio Receiver Design* (Chapman & Hall) by K. R. Sturley, BBC's Chief Engineer (Fig. 37). Volume 1 covers radio frequency amplification and detection (3rd edn., 1965); vol. 2 is concerned with audio frequency amplification, power supplies, receiver measurements, television, receiver design, etc. (2nd edn. in preparation). Each chapter includes a bibliography.

Written for radio engineers engaged in circuit design is *Frequency Modulation Engineering* by C. E. Tibbs and G. G. Johnstone, 2nd edn., 1956 (Chapman & Hall). The authoritative textbook, although dated, is *Electronic and Radio Engineering*,

FIG. 36 (*opposite*). *Radio and Television Engineers' Reference Book*. (By permission of the Buckingham Press Ltd.)

5. 2. 7. The Transistor Frequency Changer[51]. A transistor may
be used as a frequency changer by applying the oscillator voltage to
the emitter circuit and the signal to the base circuit, or both may be
inserted together in the base. It functions in a similar way to a
valve frequency changer to whose grid-cathode circuit the oscillator
voltage is applied. Frequency changing takes place because of non-
linearity between the collector current and base-emitter voltage.
Fig. 5.11 shows a suitable circuit with the oscillator voltage applied

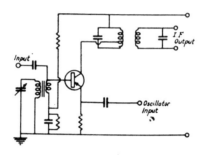

FIG. 5.11. A transistor frequency changer circuit

across a resistance (usually about 470 Ω) in the emitter circuit, and
in Fig. 5.12a is given a conversion conductance curve against oscillator peak voltage. The optimum oscillator voltage is much less than
that required for the valve, being about 0·1 volt peak. This is to be
expected because the collector voltage is so much less than the h.t.
voltage for a valve. Sometimes the frequency-changing characteristic
is plotted as conversion gain versus oscillator power input to the
frequency changer. Conversion gain is given by $10 \log_{10} P_i/P_s$, where
P_i is the power supplied to the i.f. load, and P_s is the input signal
power to the frequency changer transistor. Maximum possible conversion gain is $g_c^2/g_{0e} \cdot g_{ie}$, i.e. the frequency-changer input and
output are matched to the source and load respectively. A probable
conversion gain is 20 to 25 dB. Oscillator power is the square of the

edited by F. E. Terman and others, 4th edn., 1955 (McGraw-Hill). Principles and practice are easily summarized for the practising engineer. A reliable introductory work that has run through 9 editions since 1929 is J. A. Ratcliffe's *Physical Principles of Wireless* (1952), in the well-known Methuen's Monographs on Physical Subjects series. A good basic text, covering in particular transmitter practice, is E. K. Sandeman's *Radio Engineering* (Chapman & Hall, 2 volumes). A 3rd edition is in preparation.

A great number of publications have been written for the radio amateur. Probably the most useful are:

COLLINS, A. F. The *Radio Amateur's Handbook*, 11th edition, New York, Crowell, 1964.

NEWNES *Radio Engineer's Pocket Book*, 13th edn., 1962.

RADIO SOCIETY OF GREAT BRITAIN. *Amateur Radio Handbook*, 3rd edn., 1961. (Also: *A Guide to Amateur Radio*, 11th edn., 1965.)

Radio Organizations

International co-operation in radio communications research is the responsibility of the International Scientific Radio Union, Brussels. Activities include the negotiations of agreements on methods of measurement and the standardization of scientific measuring instruments. The Union publishes a bi-monthly *Information Bulletin*, the *Proceedings of the General Assembly* every 3 years, and a number of monographs, e.g. the *Handbook of Ionogram Interpretation and Reduction* and *Atmospheric Radio Noise*.

So far as broadcasting co-operation is concerned, there are two international bodies: the International Radio and Television Organization, Prague, with membership from eastern Europe, Asia, Africa, and Cuba; and the European Broadcasting Union. The latter publishes the *EBU Review*, which serves as an information bulletin and newsletter, and includes technical articles

---

FIG. 37 (*opposite*). Sturley's *Radio Receiver Design*. (Copyright McGraw-Hill Book Co., Inc. Used by permission.)

and abstracts, and monographs such as lists of broadcasting and television stations, a survey of VHF facilities, etc.

Two important national organizations are the Institution of Electronic and Radio Engineers and the Institute of Radio Engineers, Inc., for Great Britain and the United States respectively. The latter was amalgamated in the IEEE in 1963 (see page 66).

The Institution of Electronic and Radio Engineers, as it has been named since February 1964, started as a voluntary professional association in 1925 under the name of the Institute of Wireless Technology. In view of the increasing application of the science and techniques of radio engineering to purposes other than communication and broadcasting, the name was changed in 1941 to the British Institution of Radio Engineers. Its subject scope was broadened to include the theory, science, practice, and engineering of electronics and all kindred subjects and their applications. It is the only professional association in the United Kingdom whose essential qualification for corporate and graduate membership is an education in radio and electronic science and engineering and whose sole purpose is the promotion and advancement of those subjects.

The Institution organizes international conferences on specific subjects and operates regional sections or branches in Canada, South Africa, New Zealand, India, and Pakistan where other technical meetings take place. Recent conventions and symposia where published Proceedings have been issued include a Symposium on *Sonar Systems*, held in Birmingham University, 1962 (26 papers in one bound volume); the Convention on *Electronics and Productivity*, held in Southampton University, 1962 (32 papers in 3 volumes); a Symposium on *Cold Cathode Tubes and their Applications* (31 papers in 3 volumes); held in Cambridge University, 1964; a Symposium on *Signal Processing in Radar and Sonar Directional Systems*, held in Birmingham University, 1964 (25 papers in 1 volume); and a Symposium on *Microwave applications of Semiconductors*, held at University College, London, 1965 (35 papers in 1 volume). Other symposia are held jointly with other organizations, for example, with the Ministry of Technology, Northern Region, on *Electronic Control Systems for Industry* (1965); and with the Institution of Electrical Engineers on *Applications of Microelectronics* (1965).

The IERE also publishes regularly the monthly *Radio and Electronic Engineer* and the *Proceedings of Electronics and Radio Engineers* (6–8 issues per annum). Useful for retrospective searching is the 7th edition of *Abstracts of Papers* published in the Institution's journal from 1952 to 1963. Details are given of nearly 900 papers, reports, addresses, and contributions, arranged according to the UDC system.

The membership of the IRE was large and extended beyond the United States to Canada, Britain, and other countries. Its numerous professional activities were organized through specialist groups — Audio, Circuit Theory, Vehicle Communications, Electronic Computers, Ultrasonics Engineering, Industrial Electronics, Navigational Aids, Wave Propagation, etc. The monthly *Proceedings* included abstracts of the papers appearing in *IRE Transactions*, published separately for each of the professional groups. These activities continue under the Institute of Electrical and Electronics Engineers.

The national society for radio amateurs in the United Kingdom is the Radio Society of Great Britain, with a membership of over 12,000, some of whom live overseas. Since 1925 it has published a monthly journal the *RSGB Bulletin* which is the oldest and largest periodical in the United Kingdom devoted to amateur radio, with technical and constructional articles written by leading radio amateurs. The Society also produces many books, including the well-known *RSGB Amateur Radio Handbook*, and organizes meetings and specialized conventions throughout the country.

Radar and Microwave Techniques

The most outstanding books in this field are those in the Radiation Laboratory series, published by McGraw-Hill for the Massachusetts Institute of Technology. The 27 volumes in this ing is needed for operators of vidicon cameras to become proficient. In fact, many vidicon cameras are as easy to operate as a conventional home television receiver.

Since the vidicon camera is the first choice for most closed-circuit television systems, the remainder of this chapter is devoted to this type.

TYPES OF VIDICON CAMERAS

Two types of vidicon cameras are in popular use. The differences are not in the vidicons, but in the nature of the output signal supplied by the camera to the coaxial cable. Their identifying labels are *RF Camera* and *VF Camera*. Each offers combinations of advantages and disadvantages which are readily understood. Again, by comparison of the requirements for a specific application with the merits of the two camera types, one can make the right choice.

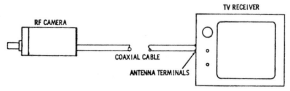

Fig. 2-3. A simple RF closed-circuit television system.

RF System

The letters "RF" are the popular abbreviation for the term *radio frequency*. Thus, an RF camera contains radio-frequency impulses similar to those transmitted by a commercial "open-circuit" television station. Because of this, the output of an RF camera can be connected directly to the antenna terminals of a conventional home television set (Fig. 2-3). No circuit modification of the television set is required. This type of overall system is referred to as an *RF system*.

It is common practice to design RF cameras so that their signals can be tuned in on Channels 2 through 6. A choice of channels is necessary so that the user can operate the camera on an unoccupied TV channel. Otherwise, interference from a commercial-TV broadcast station would result. Channels 2 through 6 are at the low-frequency end of the spectrum assigned for commercial telecasting. RF cameras are designed to operate at the lower frequencies because the camera (and all other units within the system) will operate more efficiently at these frequencies.

series consolidates much of the tremendous research work that was done during the Second World War. Two important titles that may still be regarded as valuable for reference purposes are: *Radar System Engineering*, edited L. N. Ridenour (1947) and *Radar Engineering* by D. G. Fink (1947). Volume 28 of the series, the *Index*, serves as a complete guide to the entire series and the activities of the Radiation Laboratory.

Also compiled at the MIT, and based on teaching programmes at the Radar School, is the textbook *Principles of Radar* by J. F. Reintjes and G. T. Coates, 3rd edn., 1952 (McGraw-Hill). It covers the basic concepts and techniques of transmission lines, waveguides, cavity resonators, and antennas. A more recent standard text for students, operators, and technicians is R. S. H. Boulding's *Principles and Practice of Radar*, 7th edn., 1963 (Newnes).

A branch of telecommunications that has made impressive advances is that associated with the use of the radiation band that ranges from 100 cm to 1 mm in wavelength. An intermediate level manual consolidating much of these advances is *Microwave Engineering* by A. F. Harvey (Academic Press, 1963). It is intended for the engineer practising in microwave antennas, components, electron tubes, systems, etc. Extensive bibliographies are included. An older book, useful for its bibliography of over 700 items ranging from 1929 to 1953, is *Microwave Theory and Techniques* by H. J. Reich and others (Princeton, NJ, Van Nostrand, 1953).

Television

The standard reference work covering the entire field, including basic principles, is *The Television Engineering Handbook*, edited by D. G. Fink (McGraw-Hill, 1957). Equal attention is paid to black-and-white and to colour television. References are given in each of the twenty special fields covered.

FIG. 38 (*opposite*).   *Closed Circuit Television Handbook* by Leon A. Wortman. (Published by Foulsham-Sams Technical Books. Used by permission.)

Another standard work on the subject covering fundamental principles is V. K. Zworykin and G. A. Morton's *Television: the electronics of image transmission in color and monochrome*, 2nd edn. (New York, Wiley, 1954). Mr. Zworykin, in collaboration with others, has produced a more recent text covering television equipment for research, medicine, education, defence, the home, and the farm. It is entitled *Television in Science and Industry* (Wiley, 1958).

For the development engineer a significant publication is *Television Engineering*, an edited version of the papers read at the international conference held by the Institution of Electrical Engineers in London in 1962.

A good teaching series in 4 volumes has been produced by members of the BBC Engineering Division, primarily intended for staff instruction — *Television Engineering: principles and practice* by S. W. Amos and D. C. Birkinshaw (Iliffe). Volume 1, which covers fundamentals, has been rewritten to cope with important developments, including the changeover by the British to the 625-line standard (2nd edn., 1963). Volume 2 covers video-frequency amplification (1956); Vol. 3, waveform generation (1957); Vol. 4, general circuit techniques (1958).

Current trends towards colour television and closed-circuit television are represented in M. S. Kiver's *Colour Television Fundamentals*, 2nd edn., 1964 (McGraw-Hill) and L. A. Wortman's *Closed Circuit Television Handbook* (New York, Sams, 1964 (in the UK, Foulsham, 1965). (Fig. 38).

The official organization for the furtherance of study and research in television and associated problems is the Royal Television Society, founded in 1927. It publishes quarterly the *Television Society Journal*.

Periodicals

Of the many periodicals concerned with telecommunications the following is a selection: *A. W. A. Technical Review (Australia)*; *EBU Review: Sound and Television Broadcasting News. Part A. Technical; International Broadcast Engineer* (monthly, has abstracts, British and American patent news); *Institution of Radio Engineers, Australia. Proceedings*; *Institution of Telecommunication Engineers, Delhi. Journal* (quarterly); *Journal of Research (National Bureau of Standards) Section D. Radio Science*; *Journal of the Society of Motion Picture and Television Engineers* (monthly); *Journal of the Television Society* (London, quarterly); *Onde Électrique* (Paris, monthly); *Practical Wireless* (for the hobbyist); *Proceedings of the Society of Relay Engineers*; *Radar and Electronics; Radio and Television* (Prague) (news of OIRT and contains abstracts of East European papers); *Radio Engineering* (translation of Radiotekhnika); *Radio Engineering and Electronic Physics* (trans. of *Radiotekhnika i Elektronika*); *Radio Mentor* (Berlin); *Radio Rivista* (Milan); *Radio und Fersehen* (Germany); *Reports of the Electrical Communications Laboratory, Japan* (in English); *Short Wave Magazine* (London, monthly); *Wireless World* (London, monthly).

Periodicals from Manufacturing Firms

In the telecommunications and allied fields, manufacturing firms produce some very useful periodicals.

Mullard Technical Communications (monthly), published since 1952, contains papers on research into valves, tubes and semiconductor devices. Two smaller periodicals from the same firm are *Mullard Industrial Valve Newsletter* and *Mullard Semiconductor Division: industrial news letter*, both quarterly. *Point-to-point Telecommunications* and *Sound and Vision Broadcasting* are both published by the Marconi Co. Ltd., 3 times a year.

At research level there is the *Marconi Review* (quarterly) dealing with radio and telephone engineering generally.

American publications include (in the telegraph and telephone fields): *Bell Laboratories Record* (New York); *Bell System Technical Journal* (bi-monthly); *Bell Telephone Review* (quarterly).

Other periodicals of value include *Nachrichtentecknik*; *Philips Telecommunication Review*; and *Telephone Engineer and Management* (Chicago); and *Telephony* (weekly also published in Chicago).

CHAPTER 18

Data Processing and Control Engineering
UDC 681.14

COMPUTER techniques are finding widespread applications in all branches of engineering and science. In many cases complex problems that were at one time practically insoluble are now capable of solution in a relatively short time. Complex calculations can be performed over and over again until the optimum solution is obtained. The greatest contributions currently being made are in computer applications associated with defence projects, the design of aircraft and space craft, nuclear power and chemical plant, and other complex structures. The amount of research being done — much of which is government financed — is consequently large. It is responsible for a rapidly growing volume of literature in different forms: textbooks, scientific and technical reports, articles in periodicals, conference papers, standards, and patents.

As an illustration of the extent of this literature growth, the Selective Bibliography on Computers (SB-472) issued by the Office of Technical Services, Washington, lists over 400 government agency reports and translations added to the OTS collection during the period April 1959 to September 1961. A further supplement covering the period September 1961 to February 1963 lists an additional 650 or more items. Other extensive listings issued by the same authority (now the Clearinghouse for Federal Scientific and Technical Information) include *Computer Related Research* (SB-473) covering medicine, cybernetics, artificial intelligence, speech and character recognition, reading and teaching machines, etc., *Data Processing and Programming* (SB-474); and *Information Storage and Retrieval* (SB-475). Two very useful select reading lists have been issued by HERTIS (head-quarters at the Hatfield Technical College, Hertford): *References on Mathematical Programming* (1964) and *Select Bibliography on Computer Applications in Commerce and Industry* (1963).

The rapid speed of development is also responsible for frequent meetings and conferences each yielding papers that add to the growth rate of important literature. An important series started in 1951 were the joint computer conferences sponsored by the American Institute of Electrical Engineers (now the IEEE), the Institute of Radio Engineers, and the Association for Computing Machinery. Important papers, review articles, and bibliographies were regularly featured in the *IRE Transactions on Electronic Computers* (continued as *IEEE Transactions on Electronic Computers*).

Computer design and development involves a number of disciplines. Initially planning is usually started by mathematicians, accountants, and physicists. They work out logical designs to be followed up by electronic engineers who design the circuits. Mechanical and electrical engineers may also be involved. Mathematical aspects of computers and associated literature have already been considered in John E. Pemberton's *How to Find out in Mathematics* (Pergamon Press, 1963). This chapter is intended for the student and practitioner of engineering.

The standard reference work on computers is the *Computer Handbook* (Fig. 39) edited by H. D. Husky and G. A. Korn (McGraw-Hill, 1961). It presents detailed technical information and a great amount of industrial application. Many actual circuit diagrams are included together with descriptions of significant applications. Important techniques covered are network-type analogues for fields, structures, and power systems, for mechanical, electromechanical, hydrodynamic, and heat transfer computing elements.

Comprehensive treatment for the practical engineer is also given

Section 16

DIGITAL-COMPUTER-SYSTEM DESIGN

By

WERNER BUCHHOLZ, *Senior Systems Planner, International Business Machines Corporation, Poughkeepsie, N.Y.*

WILLIAM F. GUNNING, *Vice-President—Technical Director, Epsco-West, Inc., Anaheim, Calif.*

HARRY D. HUSKEY, *Professor of Electrical Engineering and Mathematics, University of California, Berkeley, Calif.*

RAGNAR THORENSEN, *Director, Magnavox Research Laboratories, Torrance, Calif.*

CONTENTS

by G. A. and T. M. Korn in their *Electronic Analog Computers*, 2nd edn. (McGraw-Hill, 1956). A more recent book by the Korns is *Electronic Analog and Hybrid Computers* (McGraw-Hill, 1964). New applications are constantly being developed for analogue techniques, and there is a demand for ever higher speeds. Exploring some of the possibilities hitherto little developed is D. M. Mackay and M. E. Fisher in *Analogue Computing at Ultra-high Speed* (Chapman & Hall, 1962). Textbooks on computer principles design and practice are numerous. The titles included below therefore must be regarded as representative only.

As authoritative introductions for non-specialists, the Blackie's Electronic User series, is worthy of attention. Two books so far included are *Digital Techniques* by D. W. Davies of the National Physical Laboratory (1963) and *Analogue Computers* by R. Paul of the College of Aeronautics. Another reliable work at the same level is M. G. Hartley's *Introduction to Electronic Analogue Computers* (1962), one of the Methuen Monograph series. Also useful as an introduction to many recent equipment improvements and advanced techniques in C. L. Johnson's *Analog Computer Techniques*, 2nd edn. (McGraw-Hill, 1963).

On the grounds of economy, there will be many users of small or medium-sized computers only. They will need to achieve accurate results with the minimum of resources, frequently having to design and maintain their own equipment. *The Design and Use of Electronic Analogue Computers* by C. P. Gilbert (Chapman & Hall, 1964) has been written for this type of situation.

So far we have mainly discussed information on analogue computers. More extensive use is made of the digital computer which basically works in numbers rather than in other properties to denote numbers. Its ability to add, subtract, multiply, divide, and total; sort, select, and file information and print out the results, finds many applications in engineering and in commerce.

FIG. 39 (*opposite*). Husky and Korn's *Computer Handbook*. (Copyright McGraw-Hill Book Co., Inc. Used by permission.)

The volume of published literature on this aspect of data processing is naturally large and only representative works are covered here.

A broad technical introduction to the subject, covering everything from coding and components to computer applications, is *Digital Computer Systems* by S. B. Williams (McGraw-Hill, 1959). The reader requires to be familiar with electrical circuits and apparatus but only a little or no knowledge of mathematics. Design principles and functions are covered by C. V. L. Smith in *Electronic Digital Computers* (McGraw-Hill, 1959); a useful bibliography is included of over 300 references ranging from 1904 to 1957. An even more extensive list of references, totalling over 600 and covering the period 1842–1955, is given by A. D. and K. H. V. Booth in the 2nd edition of their book *Automatic Digital Computers* (New York, Academic Press, 1956). The 3rd edition (London, Butterworths), published in 1965, extends the bibliography to 1965 but it is more selective in coverage (18 pages).

Another text for the designer and carrying numerous references — over 300 from 1948 to 1957, is *Digital Computer Components and Circuits* by R. K. Richards (New York, Van Nostrand, 1957). This is a companion volume to the author's earlier work *Arithmetic Operations in Digital Computers* (1955). There is also M. Phister's *Logical Design of Digital Computers* (New York, Wiley, 1958). A more recent design book is E. L. Braun's *Digital Computer Design: logic, circuitry and synthesis* (1963).

The general trend is for ever higher speeds of operation and greater storage capacity. Introducing the problems involved in design for faster calculations is *High-Speed Data Processing* by C. C. Gotleib and J. N. P. Hume (McGraw-Hill, 1958). A modern textbook on data storage design suitable for postgraduate courses is W. Renwick's *Digital Storage Systems* (Spon, 1964). A review of present and future developments is also included.

Of the large number of introductory type textbooks available the following selection should be useful to both student and engineer alike. Covering logic design and practice and with the emphasis on commonly accepted techniques is *Digital Computer Technology* by I. H. Gould and F. S. Ellis (Chapman & Hall, 1963). Another approach from the general point of view is *The Theory and Design of Digital Machines* (McGraw-Hill, 1962). Fundamental topics of digital arithmetic, Boolean algebra, logic circuits, etc., are dealt with by Y. Chu in *Digital Computer Design Fundamentals* (McGraw-Hill, 1962). Also introducing basic principles is M. Mandl's *Fundamentals of Digital Computers* (Prentice-Hall, 1958), and R. S. Ledley's *Digital Computer and Control Engineering* (McGraw-Hill, 1960), a first-year graduate text.

The broader field of automatic control is covered in its many aspects by a very large literature, but there are two good general handbooks that should be useful in a technical library. Newnes' *Automatic Control Handbook*, edited by G. A. T. Burdett (1962), gives detailed consideration of automatic control mechanisms, components, and processes. Among the many subjects covered are: electric motors, relays and solenoids, switching, electric servo systems, amplifiers, voltage control, tubes and transistors, materials, cables and wiring, transducers, nucleonic switching, etc.

Representing American design philosophy is the *Handbook of Automation, Computation and Control*, edited by E. M. Grabbe and others (New York, Wiley, 1958–61) in 3 volumes. With contributions from a large number of specialists, the purpose of the book is to gather together in one place the available theory and information on general mathematics, feedback control, computers, data processing, and systems design, but with the emphasis on practical application. The reader is assumed to have some engineering training.

Organizations

The value of societies in the dissemination of significant information cannot be overstressed. Computer techniques are well covered in this respect both at international and national levels. The Provisional International Computation Centre,

Rome, convened by Unesco in 1956, is serving a very useful purpose in co-ordinating the work of other organizations.

In addition to reporting on its own activities, its *Bulletin* also covers those of member countries. Details of national computer societies can also be supplied. The Centre has also published a useful multilingual glossary and proceedings on various symposia relating to computers and mathematical methods. Another organization of value is the International Association for Analog Computation, formed in Brussels in 1955 (see below under "periodicals").

The two representative societies for Great Britain and the United States are the British Computer Society in London and the Association for Computing Machinery in Baltimore. The British society publishes regularly *Computer Journal* (see below). The ACM is responsible for the bi-monthly *Computing Reviews* and *Communications*.

An important organization in a related field is the International Federation of Automatic Control (IFAC), founded in Dusseldorf in 1957. Its membership consists of 30 countries each represented by one scientific or professional engineering organization, or a similar body. The United Kingdom representative, for example, is the United Kingdom Automation Council (c/o the Institution of Electrical Engineers); in USA it is the American Automatic Control Council (c/o Brooklyn Polytechnic Institute). The work of IFAC is implemented by various technical committees. One is concerned with education, others compile information on terminology and symbols, or are responsible for the bibliographies published in IFAC's *Information Bulletin* (1958–   ).

Very important are the published proceedings of the triennial congresses. The first International Congress held in Moscow, 1960, resulted in 4 volumes with summaries in English, French, and German (Butterworths, 1961); the second in Basle, 1963, yielded 2 volumes (also Butterworths). IFAC members are also very active with symposia. In 1956 alone there were four — in Stavanger, Tokyo, Teddington, and Munich — concerned with automatic control in the peaceful uses of space, control system design, the theory of self-adaptive control systems, and microminiaturization.

Dictionaries, Encyclopedias and Directories

Elsevier's Dictionary of Automatic Control (1963), edited by W. E. Clason, is arranged on an English–American alphabetical base with equivalents, and indexes in French, German and Russian. A *Dictionary of Automatic Control* by R. J. Bibbero (Reinhold, 1960), on the other hand, is a list of explanations and discussions in English of important topics and terms in the field. ASME Standard 105 (1954) is on *Automatic Control Terminology* and includes diagrams where useful to clarify definitions.

Another Elsevier work, *Elsevier's Dictionary of Automation, Computers, Control and Measuring* (1961), gives some 3390 terms in English–American with French, German, Spanish, Italian, and Dutch translations and reverse keys. Another polyglot dictionary is *Terminology of Electronic Data Processing*, edited by the Comité Européen des Assurances and published by Konrad Triltsch, Würzburg, in 1962. Each language section (English, French, German, Spanish, and Italian) has an encyclopedic subsection and a lexicon.

Data Processing Equipment Encyclopedia is a 2-volume work published by Gille Associates, Detroit, in 1961, which provides data and illustrations on American equipment with some useful historical notes. *Manual of Computer Systems*, ed. by B. A. Maynard (1964–   ), is a loose-leaf directory.

Trade directories include *Sell's Automation, Electronics, Nuclear Engineering*; and *Instruments, Electronics, Automation* (both British publications): *Electronic Engineers Master* for the United States and *Automatik ABC* published in Hamburg by R. V. Decker's Verlag, G. Schenck GmbH.

Periodicals on Data Processing

The British Computer Society publishes *The Computer Journal*, quarterly, containing research level papers, correspondence; and useful book reviews. The Society also produces quarterly *The Computer Bulletin*, which has articles of a more general nature, notes and news, book reviews, correspondence, and lists of additions to the library of the Society (which is situated in the Leicester College of Technology).

The IEEE Computer Group produces *IEEE Transactions on Electronic Computers*, bi-monthly, which, in addition to its major papers, short notes, and correspondence, includes abstracts of current computer literature, reviews of books and papers in the computer field and information retrieval cards (abstracts of its own papers).

The United States equivalent of the BCS, the Association for Computing Machinery, produces three publications: *The Journal of the Association for Computing Machinery* (quarterly) with specialized papers; *Communications of the ACM*, a scientific monthly with articles of interest to the whole (or most of the) membership, including correspondence, news, announcements, and advertisements; and *Computing Reviews* (see under "abstracts" below).

There are several trade and technical journals in both Britain and America which are devoted to data processing. These include (British): *Data Processing* (bi-monthly, Iliffe Publications); *Computer Survey* (a statistical and analytical journal, bi-monthly); *Data and Control* (monthly, Business Publications Ltd.). (American): *Computer Design* (monthly); *Computers and Automation* (monthly); *Datamation* (monthly); *Data Processing Magazine* (monthly); *Journal of Data Management* (monthly) (published by the Data Processing Management Association).

The International Computation Centre, Rome (described above), publishes its quarterly *ICC Bulletin* with research level articles as well as book reviews, notes and news, etc.

The Proceedings of the International Association for Analog

Computation is published quarterly and is the official journal of the Association whose headquarters are in Brussels. Contributions are in English or French and there are summaries in other languages. A bibliography of books and papers is a regular feature.

From France is the *Electro Calcul*, while among German periodicals dealing with data processing are: *ADL–Nachrichten* (bi-monthly); *Elektronische Datenverarbeitung* (bi-monthly with English abstracts of its articles); *Elektronische Rechenanlagen* (bi-monthly); *Mathematik Technik Wirtschaft* (quarterly).

BIT is a quarterly publication of the Nordisk Tidskrift for Informationsbehandling in which most of the papers are in English.

Calcolo is a quarterly journal published jointly by three Italian data processing organizations: some of the contributions, which are highly specialized, are in English.

Two newsletters are *Digital Computer Newsletter* published quarterly by the US Office of Naval Research and the slighter *Computer News* published monthly by Technical Information Co. Ltd., Jersey. *Computer Weekly* started in September, 1966.

Amongst useful house journals and technical journals produced by manufacturing firms are *ICT Data Processing Journal* and *De La Rue Bull System*.

Abstracts

Computer Abstracts contains about 3000 abstracts per year from world literature and includes books. An annual subject and author index is published together with a patent index. *Control Abstracts* and *Current Papers on Control* both started in 1966, published as part of *Science Abstracts*.

Computing Reviews, a bimonthly publication of the Association for Computing Machinery is intended to furnish critical information about all current publications in any area of the computing sciences and therefore carries evaluative reviews of books, articles, reports and other media: its net is cast very widely.

The *Abstracts of Current Computer Literature*, which appear as part of the bi-monthly *IEEE Transactions on Electronic Computers*, cover upwards of 600 papers and reports a year. These are actually prepared on a commercial basis by Cambridge Communications Corpn., Cambridge, Mass., which is also responsible for two abstracts journals — *Solid State Abstracts* and *Information Processing Journal* — and two card services — *Solid State Abstracts on Cards* and *Computer Abstracts on Cards*. *Information Processing Journal* appears in 12 numbers per year although various issues may be combined. An annual cumulated subject index is bound in with each No. 12.

An indexing service with subject tracings in both German and English is the quarterly *Titel von Veröffentlichungen über Analog-und Ziffernrechner und Ihre Anwendungen* (Current Bibliography on Analog and Digital Computers and their Applications), jointly edited by the Deutsche Forschungsgemeinschaft and the International Computation Center, Rome

Periodicals on Control Engineering

At research level, periodicals on control engineering include *The International Journal of Control* (monthly), formerly known as the *Journal of Electronics and Control*, which includes scholarly contributions from many countries. It is published in London. *Automatica, the International Journal on Automatic Control and Automation* is a quarterly Pergamon journal which likewise has international contributions on the results of research and development. Papers may be published in either English, French, German, or Russian with summaries in the other three languages, but in practice English language articles predominate.

The IEEE Transactions on Automatic Control appears quarterly and contains upwards of 8 major papers, many shorter papers, and correspondence. *Information and Control* is bi-monthly and contains highly specialized, often mathematical, papers. It is published by the Academic Press, New York, who are also responsible for *Progress in Control Engineering* (Vol. 1, 1962;

Vol. 2, 1964), containing survey and review articles of progress in the field. A similar service is performed by Pergamon's *Annual Review in Automatic Programming* (Vol. 3, 1963, etc.) and by *Advances in Control Systems* (Vol. 1, 1964). *IFAC Information Bulletin*, which appears twice a year, is the official news organ of the International Federation of Automatic Control. It is in English and is distributed by the IFAC Secretary from Düsseldorf, West Germany. In addition to the large résumés of papers already presented at IFAC meetings, it includes information on future activities and reviews of publications.

In Italian is *Automazione e Strumentazione*, the monthly journal of ANIPLA, the Associazione Nazionale Italiana per L'Automazione, and containing main articles, notes and news, etc., and many advertisements. The official monthly journal of the Association Française de Régulation et d'Automatisme is *Automatisme*. A French trade journal, well illustrated and containing many advertisements, is the monthly *Mesures · Régulation · Automatisme*.

From West Germany is published *Regelungstechnik* with a monthly bibliography of relevant papers and reports and with abstracts of its own articles in English.

Messen–Steuern–Regeln (monthly) is the official organ of the DGMA (Deutschen Gesellschaft für Messtechnik und Automatisierung) and it also contains a regular bibliography and has abstracts of its own major papers in English, French, Russian, and German. *Regelungstechnische Praxis* is another West German publication.

Several flourishing trade journals are published in the United Kingdom and in the United States. *Control and Automation Progress* (monthly, Morgan Bros.); *Process Control and Automation* (monthly, Guardian Technical Journals Ltd.); and *Instrument and Control Engineering* (monthly, Tothill Press) are all British, while from America come *Control Engineering* and *Automation* (both also monthly).

A cover-to-cover translation of the Russian journal *Automatika i Telemekhanika* is sponsored by the Instrument Society of America under the title *Automation and Remote Control*. The monthly translated version which appears about 5 months after the publication of the original enables an account to be kept of Russian work in the field.

Reflecting their interests in the prospects and practicalities of automatic controls, are a number of periodicals published in the East European countries. From Poland come *Pomiary, Automatyka, Kontrola* (Measurements, Automation and Control) (monthly); and *Archiwum Automatyki i Telemechaniki* (Archives of Automatics and Telemechanics), the quarterly journal of the Automation Laboratory, Polish Academy of Sciences, containing summaries of articles in English, French, German, or Russian.

Automatica si Electronica (Automation and Electronics) is a bi-monthly journal issued by the Scientific Association of Engineers and Technicians of Rumania, with English, French, German, and Russian summaries. Also from Bucharest comes *Probleme de Automatizare* (Problems of Automation) published irregularly.

Index

In addition to normal subject terms, entries have been made for most of the titles referred to in the text. Serial publications are distinguished, where necessary, by the addition of jnl. after the title, book titles are followed by the author(s) surname(s). It is assumed that the predominate use of this guide to the literature will be for subject searches, consequently periodical titles starting with *Journal of* and *Transactions of* are entered either directly under the name of the issuing society or under a more helpful initial keyword. For the same reason some of the book titles have been transposed. Authors' names, however, have also been included to help those readers who may have the need for this approach.

STURLEY, K. R.   187

STURMEY, S. G.   134

Subject Collections in European Libraries   29

SUCHER, M. and Fox, J.   152

SUHNER, F.   114

SUSSKIND, C.   177

Tables   113–16

Tables, bibliographies   115–16

Tables of Constants and Numerical Data   114

Tables of Physical and Chemical Constants (Kaye)   114

Tables, Russian   116

TAPIA, E. W.   21

Teaching methods   107

Technical Book Review (jnl.)   37

Technical Book Review Index (jnl.)   37

Technical Books in Print (annual)   33

Technical Data on Fuel (Spiers)   115

Technical Dictionary of the Terms used in Electrical Engineering (Thali)   59

Technical Translations (jnl.)   62

Technical Translations, List of (Canada)   63

Technique of Microwave Measurements (Montgomery)   152

Technique of Radio Design (Zepler)   187

Technisches Zentralblatt (German abstracts jnl.)   78

Abteilung Engeriewesen   150

Technological Abstracts Originating in the British Commonwealth (DSIR)   80

Telcon Story   133

Telecommunication engineering   183

history   133

Telecommunication Journal   183, 185

Telegraph Construction and Maintenance Co.   133

Telegraph Engineers, Society: *Journal*   65

Telemetry (IEEE Transactions)   181

Telephone directories   84

Telephones, history   133

Television   193

Television (Zworykin and Morton)   194

Television Engineering (Amos)   194

Television Engineering conference (IEE)   194

Television Engineering Handbook (Fink)   193

Television in Science and Industry (Zworykin)   194

Television receivers (IEEE Transactions)   181

Television Society, Royal   97, 195

Television, standards   51

Telex directories   84

TERMAN, F. E. and PETTIT, J. M.   151

TERMAN, F. E., and others   189

Terrell and Shelley on Patents   126

Textbooks   44–46

Textbook in Print (annual)   108

THALI, H.   59

Theory of Electromagnetism (Jones)   167

Theory of Networks and Lines (Potter and Fich)   167

Thermionic Valves, 1904–1954   133 (IEE)

Theses   108

Theses, bibliographies   110

THEWLIS, J.   55–57

Thomas' Register of American Manufacturers   84, 130

THOMSON, SIR J. T.   170

THORNTON, J. L.   134

TIBBS, C. E. and JOHNSTONE, G. G.   187

Titel von Veroffentlichungen über Analog-und Ziffernrechner und Ihre Andwendeungen (German indexing jnl.)   206

TOASE, M.   70

Toshiba Review (Japanese house jnl.)   68

Trade literature   128